ONE-A-WEEK
Mental Arithmetic Te
Book 3

C000241052

William Hartley

Contents

Introduction

One-a-Week Mental Arithmetic Tests have been designed to address the needs of busy teachers by providing a valuable resource for practising and developing mental arithmetic skills. This book is one of a series of four aimed at the 7–11 age-range.

All four books aim to:
- improve the accuracy and speed with which the children carry out essential basic calculations
- help encourage the development of listening skills and independent working.

This book is split into five sections: A, B, C, D and E. Sections A, B and C each have 40 exercises with answers provided and are **not** intended for direct use by the children. Each exercise contains ten quick-fire questions. Section A has 3-element questions; section B has 4-element questions; section C has 5-element questions. These questions should be asked orally from left to right in the order given but some effort should be made to vary delivery and teach relevant points as they arise. The children could write the answers or give a verbal response.

Sections D and E are photocopiable activity sheets of mathematical trails, intended for either individual or whole class use. Section D has 13-element trails; section E has 17-element trails. The trails could also be used orally with more able children when only the final answer is required. The answers to sections D and E can be found at the back of the book.

Weekly tests could be provided by combining the exercises in various ways, such as one exercise from section A, B or C plus one from section D or E. Various other combinations are possible depending on the age and ability of the children.

It is not intended that the children should do any written calculations when doing the exercises. Only the answers should be written down. However, some teachers might find it helpful for their children to have access to calculation aids such as table sheets, addition squares, number lines or, under certain circumstances, pocket calculators. As the children progress, the challenge of working against the clock could also be introduced.

Mathematical Range: The vast majority of calculations contained within the exercises of this book fit into the mathematical range as outlined below:

Addition - adding of numbers with totals up to 80.

Subtraction - subtracting of numbers 0 to 15 from numbers up to 90.

Multiplication - multiplying by numbers 2 to 9 up to and including 12 x 9 = 108.

Division - dividing by numbers 2 to 9 up to and including 108 ÷ 9 = 12.

Within this *mathematical range* the exercises in each section are grouped into stages according to difficulty with Stage 1 exercises being the easiest and Stage 4 the hardest. On the *Equivalency Chart* below horizontal movement keeps you in the same stage but either increases or decreases the number of calculations in each exercise. The animal coding between each stage and each exercise helps to identify at a glance the status of any exercise in the book. It also allows you to link quickly the *Teacher Exercises* and the *Children's Worksheets*.

EQUIVALENCY CHART
for all sections

Stage	Teacher Exercises			Children's Worksheets	
	Section A 3 - Element	Section B 4 - Element	Section C 5 - Element	Section D 13 - Element	Section E 17 - Element
1	Exercises A1 - A8	Exercises B1 - B8	Exercises C1 - C8	Exercises D1 - D8	Exercises E1 - E8
2	Exercises A9 - A16	Exercises B9 - B16	Exercises C9 - C16	Exercises D9 - D16	Exercises E9 - E16
3	Exercises A17 - A24	Exercises B17 - B24	Exercises C17 - C24	Exercises D17 - D24	Exercises E17 - E24
4	Exercises A25 - A32	Exercises B25- B32	Exercises C25 - C32	Exercises D25 - D32	Exercises E25 - E32
Revision	Exercises A33 - A40	Exercises B33 - B40	Exercises C33- C40	Exercises D33- D40	Exercises E33- E40

Section A

Exercise A1

1 39 = 3 + 9 + ☐
2 28 + 6 - ☐ = 26
3 24 ÷ 4 x ☐ = 54
4 60 = ☐ x 5 x 6
5 32 ÷ 4 ÷ ☐ = 2
6 ☐ = 45 ÷ 5 + 28
7 4 x 9 - ☐ = 28
8 ☐ = 8 x 4 - 3
9 27 = 44 - ☐ - 7
10 38 - 9 + 5 = ☐

Exercise A2

1 ☐ = 40 ÷ 4 ÷ 5
2 6 x 6 ÷ 6 = ☐
3 ☐ = 48 ÷ 6 ÷ 4
4 28 + 4 + 6 = ☐
5 26 = 38 - ☐ - 7
6 41 - 8 - ☐ = 30
7 39 - ☐ - 6 = 27
8 ☐ = 8 + 21 + 4
9 72 = 4 x 3 x ☐
10 ☐ = 30 ÷ 5 x 7

	Ex 1	Ex 2
1	27	2
2	8	6
3	9	2
4	2	38
5	4	5
6	37	3
7	8	6
8	29	33
9	10	6
10	34	42

Exercise A3

1 24 + 7 + 6 = ☐
2 100 ÷ 10 ÷ ☐ = 2
3 40 = 2 x 5 x ☐
4 4 x 3 x ☐ = 48
5 38 = 36 - 7 + ☐
6 ☐ = 23 + 5 ÷ 4
7 32 ÷ 4 ÷ 4 = ☐
8 ☐ = 6 x 2 ÷ 4
9 48 ÷ 6 + 24 = ☐
10 38 = ☐ + 7 + 26

Exercise A4

1 3 = 60 ÷ 5 ÷ ☐
2 2 x 4 x ☐ = 48
3 ☐ = 24 + 8 - 3
4 33 - 6 - ☐ = 22
5 2 x 4 x 5 = ☐
6 42 - 9 - ☐ = 31
7 26 + 9 ÷ 5 = ☐
8 ☐ = 3 + 24 + 8
9 ☐ = 7 x 6 - 7
10 8 x 5 - 8 = ☐

	Ex 3	Ex 4
1	37	4
2	5	6
3	4	29
4	4	5
5	9	40
6	7	2
7	2	7
8	3	35
9	32	35
10	5	32

Exercise A5

1 24 + ☐ + 6 = 35
2 ☐ = 35 - 8 + 3
3 38 = 6 x 7 - ☐
4 ☐ = 5 x 5 + 7
5 24 = 27 + ☐ - 10
6 12 ÷ 3 - 2 = ☐
7 ☐ = 23 + 7 - 8
8 28 = 30 - 7 + ☐
9 21 + 7 ÷ ☐ = 7
10 ☐ = 32 ÷ 4 - 5

Exercise A6

1 7 + ☐ + 7 = 35
2 45 ÷ 5 + ☐ = 35
3 ☐ = 42 ÷ 6 + 22
4 9 = 28 + 8 ÷ ☐
5 40 ÷ 4 x 5 = ☐
6 31 - 6 ÷ ☐ = 5
7 44 - 4 - 5 = ☐
8 54 ÷ 6 x 5 = ☐
9 ☐ = 7 x 6 - 6
10 4 x 9 - ☐ = 28

	Ex 5	Ex 6
1	5	21
2	30	26
3	4	29
4	32	4
5	7	50
6	2	5
7	22	35
8	5	45
9	4	36
10	3	8

	Ex 7	Ex 8
1	34	6
2	9	6
3	4	6
4	8	28
5	9	4
6	5	7
7	6	10
8	30	23
9	7	2
10	32	66

Exercise A7

1. $4 \times 10 - 6 = \square$
2. $33 - 6 + \square = 36$
3. $24 + 6 - \square = 26$
4. $32 = 4 \times 10 - \square$
5. $9 \times 5 - \square = 36$
6. $\square = 24 + 6 \div 6$
7. $32 - 10 + \square = 28$
8. $30 \div 6 + 25 = \square$
9. $29 + 5 - \square = 27$
10. $\square = 24 \div 4 + 26$

Exercise A8

1. $4 + 26 \div \square = 5$
2. $\square = 9 \times 4 \div 6$
3. $4 \times 6 \div 4 = \square$
4. $\square = 5 \times 4 + 8$
5. $28 = 35 \div 5 \times \square$
6. $\square = 72 \div 6 - 5$
7. $2 = 5 \times 4 \div \square$
8. $\square = 37 - 6 - 8$
9. $3 \times 4 \div 6 = \square$
10. $\square = 55 \div 5 \times 6$

	Ex 9	Ex 10
1	40	9
2	8	48
3	39	6
4	38	84
5	6	45
6	63	41
7	5	3
8	6	72
9	63	43
10	32	5

Exercise A9

1. $\square = 53 - 7 - 6$
2. $59 - \square - 4 = 47$
3. $50 - 2 - 9 = \square$
4. $\square = 41 - 7 + 4$
5. $2 \times 6 \times \square = 72$
6. $54 \div 6 \times 7 = \square$
7. $38 + \square + 3 = 46$
8. $8 = 39 + 9 \div \square$
9. $\square = 3 \times 3 \times 7$
10. $8 \times 5 - 8 = \square$

Exercise A10

1. $38 = 31 + \square - 2$
2. $\square = 6 + 35 + 7$
3. $72 \div 6 \div \square = 2$
4. $\square = 6 \times 2 \times 7$
5. $\square = 33 + 5 + 7$
6. $54 \div 6 + 32 = \square$
7. $36 = 47 - \square - 8$
8. $3 \times 4 \times 6 = \square$
9. $30 + 4 + 9 = \square$
10. $47 - 8 + \square = 44$

	Ex 11	Ex 12
1	6	2
2	12	4
3	4	5
4	46	29
5	37	7
6	3	5
7	44	6
8	6	41
9	6	8
10	70	40

Exercise A11

1. $48 = 40 \div 5 \times \square$
2. $6 \times 10 \div 5 = \square$
3. $40 \div 5 \div \square = 2$
4. $\square = 7 + 5 + 34$
5. $\square = 6 \times 7 - 5$
6. $44 = 53 - 6 - \square$
7. $\square = 53 - 3 - 6$
8. $46 = 32 + 8 + \square$
9. $84 \div 7 \div \square = 2$
10. $5 \times 2 \times 7 = \square$

Exercise A12

1. $50 \div 5 \div 5 = \square$
2. $\square = 48 \div 4 \div 3$
3. $36 + 8 - \square = 39$
4. $\square = 43 - 6 - 8$
5. $\square = 5 \times 7 \div 5$
6. $2 = 50 \div 5 \div \square$
7. $35 + 7 \div 7 = \square$
8. $\square = 21 \div 7 + 38$
9. $57 - 9 - \square = 40$
10. $2 \times 4 \times 5 = \square$

Exercise A13

1. $\square$ = 30 + 5 ÷ 7
2. 46 - 8 + $\square$ = 44
3. 8 = 60 - 4 ÷ $\square$
4. 36 + 9 - $\square$ = 40
5. $\square$ = 36 ÷ 6 + 37
6. $\square$ = 4 + 4 x 7
7. 6 x 5 + $\square$ = 39
8. $\square$ = 48 ÷ 6 x 7
9. 10 = 10 x 7 ÷ $\square$
10. 3 + 6 x $\square$ = 45

Exercise A14

1. 12 x 5 ÷ 10 = $\square$
2. 24 ÷ 6 x $\square$ = 28
3. 63 ÷ 7 - 4 = $\square$
4. $\square$ = 8 x 7 - 8
5. 12 = 12 x 10 ÷ $\square$
6. 38 + 6 - 2 = $\square$
7. $\square$ = 7 x 7 - 6
8. 32 = 44 - 4 - $\square$
9. 43 - 7 + $\square$ = 44
10. 6 x 9 - 2 = $\square$

	Ex 13	Ex 14
1	5	6
2	6	7
3	7	5
4	5	48
5	43	10
6	56	42
7	9	43
8	56	8
9	7	8
10	5	52

Exercise A15

1. 11 = 58 - 3 ÷ $\square$
2. 36 + 6 ÷ $\square$ = 7
3. 10 ÷ 5 + 39 = $\square$
4. $\square$ = 34 + 7 - 3
5. 63 ÷ 7 - 5 = $\square$
6. $\square$ = 10 + 2 x 6
7. 14 ÷ 7 x 6 = $\square$
8. $\square$ = 5 x 7 + 7
9. 6 x 6 + $\square$ = 42
10. 6 x 5 ÷ 5 = $\square$

Exercise A16

1. $\square$ = 50 - 10 ÷ 5
2. 5 x 8 - $\square$ = 31
3. 50 - 5 ÷ 5 = $\square$
4. 7 x 6 - $\square$ = 35
5. $\square$ = 18 ÷ 6 - 3
6. 5 x 6 + $\square$ = 33
7. $\square$ = 44 - 8 + 5
8. $\square$ = 32 + 8 - 5
9. 51 - $\square$ - 7 = 40
10. 40 = 2 + $\square$ + 32

	Ex 15	Ex 16
1	5	8
2	6	9
3	41	9
4	38	7
5	4	0
6	72	3
7	12	41
8	42	35
9	6	4
10	6	6

Exercise A17

1. $\square$ = 21 + 24 + 6
2. 41 + 14 - 7 = $\square$
3. 18 + 3 ÷ 7 = $\square$
4. 13 + $\square$ + 6 = 40
5. $\square$ = 8 x 7 - 7
6. 2 x 2 x 8 = $\square$
7. 6 x 6 ÷ $\square$ = 12
8. $\square$ = 2 x 4 x 7
9. 24 + 8 + $\square$ = 54
10. 56 - $\square$ - 9 = 43

Exercise A18

1. 120 ÷ 10 x $\square$ = 96
2. $\square$ = 56 ÷ 8 x 6
3. $\square$ = 40 ÷ 8 + 22
4. 6 = 96 ÷ 8 ÷ $\square$
5. 50 - 10 x $\square$ = 120
6. 59 = 72 - 5 - $\square$
7. 64 = 61 - 5 + $\square$
8. 50 - 9 + $\square$ = 47
9. 84 ÷ 7 ÷ 4 = $\square$
10. 48 ÷ 6 x 3 = $\square$

	Ex 17	Ex 18
1	51	8
2	48	42
3	3	27
4	21	2
5	49	3
6	32	8
7	3	8
8	56	6
9	22	3
10	4	24

	Ex 19	Ex 20
1	7	49
2	25	6
3	3	8
4	42	6
5	53	8
6	45	3
7	4	8
8	36	2
9	11	10
10	35	88

Exercise A19

1 ☐ = 5 x 7 ÷ 5
2 63 ÷ 7 + ☐ = 34
3 60 - 10 x ☐ = 150
4 ☐ = 3 x 2 x 7
5 5 + 25 + 23 = ☐
6 ☐ = 36 + 14 - 5
7 8 x 6 ÷ ☐ = 12
8 70 ÷ 10 + ☐ = 43
9 ☐ = 3 + 41 ÷ 4
10 48 ÷ 8 + 29 = ☐

Exercise A20

1 64 - 6 - 9 = ☐
2 66 = 8 x 9 - ☐
3 63 - ☐ - 7 = 48
4 61 = 74 - ☐ - 7
5 4 x 2 x ☐ = 64
6 3 = 72 ÷ 8 ÷ ☐
7 7 + 49 ÷ ☐ = 7
8 ☐ = 80 ÷ 10 ÷ 4
9 9 x 7 - ☐ = 53
10 ☐ = 22 - 11 x 8

	Ex 21	Ex 22
1	43	5
2	2	63
3	10	8
4	4	22
5	12	6
6	57	8
7	60	200
8	3	8
9	9	7
10	59	45

Exercise A21

1 ☐ = 58 - 6 - 9
2 70 - 10 x ☐ = 120
3 6 x 5 ÷ ☐ = 3
4 48 ÷ 6 ÷ 2 = ☐
5 ☐ = 6 x 8 ÷ 4
6 32 + 32 - 7 = ☐
7 ☐ = 7 x 7 + 11
8 6 x 9 - ☐ = 51
9 58 - 5 + ☐ = 62
10 ☐ = 55 - 10 + 14

Exercise A22

1 13 + 17 ÷ ☐ = 6
2 ☐ = 73 - 4 - 6
3 49 = 24 + 33 - ☐
4 35 + ☐ + 4 = 61
5 50 - 8 ÷ ☐ = 7
6 4 x 3 x ☐ = 96
7 27 + 23 x 4 = ☐
8 ☐ = 7 x 8 ÷ 7
9 16 + 12 ÷ ☐ = 4
10 49 ÷ 7 + 38 = ☐

	Ex 23	Ex 24
1	80	58
2	7	53
3	45	6
4	15	2
5	10	7
6	80	8
7	59	7
8	45	15
9	4	6
10	8	8

Exercise A23

1 17 - 7 x 8 = ☐
2 8 x 7 - ☐ = 49
3 ☐ = 32 + 21 - 8
4 7 x 6 + ☐ = 57
5 66 ÷ 6 x ☐ = 110
6 17 - 7 x 8 = ☐
7 6 x 6 + 23 = ☐
8 ☐ = 32 + 21 - 8
9 ☐ = 72 ÷ 6 ÷ 3
10 52 = 6 x 10 - ☐

Exercise A24

1 6 x 11 - 8 = ☐
2 ☐ = 63 - 2 - 8
3 2 x 6 x ☐ = 72
4 ☐ = 30 ÷ 5 - 4
5 75 - 5 ÷ 10 = ☐
6 52 = 6 x 10 - ☐
7 8 x 7 - ☐ = 49
8 7 x 6 + ☐ = 57
9 10 = 26 + 34 ÷ ☐
10 26 + ☐ + 15 = 49

	Exercise A25		Exercise A26		Ex 25	Ex 26

Exercise A25

1. 51 + 21 ÷ 9 = ☐
2. ☐ = 90 ÷ 10 ÷ 3
3. 24 + 53 - 12 = ☐
4. ☐ = 8 + 18 + 22
5. 12 = 4 x 9 ÷ ☐
6. 108 ÷ 9 ÷ 4 = ☐
7. ☐ = 76 - 12 - 11
8. 11 x 8 - 14 = ☐
9. 80 - 14 + ☐ = 73
10. 63 = 33 + 41 - ☐

Exercise A26

1. 9 x 5 ÷ ☐ = 9
2. ☐ = 6 x 8 ÷ 4
3. 54 = 48 ÷ 6 + ☐
4. ☐ = 22 + 13 ÷ 7
5. 17 - 5 x ☐ = 84
6. ☐ = 24 - 15 x 7
7. 90 - ☐ - 14 = 66
8. ☐ = 84 - 12 - 11
9. 81 = 3 x 3 x ☐
10. 32 ÷ 8 x ☐ = 28

	Ex 25	Ex 26
1	8	5
2	3	12
3	65	46
4	48	5
5	3	7
6	3	63
7	53	10
8	74	61
9	7	9
10	11	7

Exercise A27

1. 43 + 7 + ☐ = 69
2. 55 = ☐ + 27 + 21
3. 88 - ☐ - 14 = 62
4. 67 = 10 x 8 - ☐
5. 67 - 13 + 8 = ☐
6. ☐ + 21 + 32 = 59
7. ☐ = 24 ÷ 8 x 9
8. 3 x 2 x 9 = ☐
9. 99 ÷ 9 + 53 = ☐
10. 19 + 21 ÷ ☐ = 5

Exercise A28

1. 20 - 14 x 7 = ☐
2. ☐ = 11 x 7 - 11
3. 54 = 58 + 11 - ☐
4. ☐ = 67 - 14 + 25
5. 56 ÷ 8 x ☐ = 63
6. ☐ = 70 ÷ 7 ÷ 5
7. ☐ = 42 ÷ 6 + 34
8. 64 ÷ 8 ÷ 4 = ☐
9. 2 x 4 x ☐ = 64
10. 36 = 2 x 3 x ☐

	Ex 27	Ex 28
1	19	42
2	7	66
3	12	15
4	13	78
5	62	9
6	6	2
7	27	41
8	54	2
9	64	8
10	8	6

Exercise A29

1. 43 + 24 - 12 = ☐
2. 8 x 9 + ☐ = 77
3. ☐ = 26 - 14 x 9
4. 3 x 7 + 47 = ☐
5. 90 = 2 x ☐ x 9
6. ☐ = 46 + 23 - 13
7. 18 ÷ 9 + 49 = ☐
8. 2 = 42 ÷ 7 ÷ ☐
9. 14 + 52 - ☐ = 55
10. ☐ = 73 - 10 ÷ 7

Exercise A30

1. 7 x 8 + 13 = ☐
2. 81 ÷ 9 ÷ ☐ = 3
3. ☐ = 8 x 10 ÷ 10
4. 69 = 24 + 31 + ☐
5. 17 + 13 x ☐ = 90
6. 31 - 15 x 2 = ☐
7. ☐ = 77 ÷ 11 x 7
8. 66 - 12 ÷ ☐ = 6
9. ☐ = 8 x 9 - 15
10. 28 ÷ 4 - 3 = ☐

	Ex 29	Ex 30
1	55	69
2	5	3
3	108	8
4	68	14
5	5	3
6	56	32
7	51	49
8	3	9
9	11	57
10	9	4

	Ex 31	Ex 32
1	9	2
2	64	66
3	65	30
4	15	25
5	73	9
6	9	4
7	67	40
8	31	2
9	16	7
10	9	11

Exercise A31

1. $19 - 11 \times \boxed{} = 72$
2. $24 + 34 + 6 = \boxed{}$
3. $\boxed{} = 23 + 54 - 12$
4. $92 - 12 - \boxed{} = 65$
5. $\boxed{} = 7 \times 8 + 17$
6. $41 + 31 \div \boxed{} = 8$
7. $22 + 13 + 32 = \boxed{}$
8. $\boxed{} = 72 \div 9 + 23$
9. $74 - 12 + \boxed{} = 78$
10. $\boxed{} = 11 + 25 \div 4$

Exercise A32

1. $10 \times 7 \times \boxed{} = 140$
2. $54 \div 6 + 57 = \boxed{}$
3. $\boxed{} = 3 + 12 \times 2$
4. $59 = 17 \times 2 + \boxed{}$
5. $49 \div 7 \times \boxed{} = 63$
6. $2 \times 18 \div \boxed{} = 9$
7. $\boxed{} = 4 \times 2 \times 5$
8. $108 \div 9 \div 6 = \boxed{}$
9. $\boxed{} = 69 - 13 \div 8$
10. $86 - \boxed{} - 15 = 60$

	Ex 33	Ex 34
1	48	9
2	5	81
3	42	64
4	12	41
5	24	35
6	32	74
7	3	5
8	13	8
9	38	96
10	8	42

Exercise A33

1. $\boxed{} = 63 - 8 - 7$
2. $22 = 33 - 6 - \boxed{}$
3. $30 \div 5 \times 7 = \boxed{}$
4. $\boxed{} = 6 \times 10 \div 5$
5. $32 = 48 \div 6 + \boxed{}$
6. $54 \div 6 + \boxed{} = 41$
7. $150 = 60 - 10 \times \boxed{}$
8. $10 \times 8 - \boxed{} = 67$
9. $41 - 7 + 4 = \boxed{}$
10. $\boxed{} + 18 + 22 = 48$

Exercise A34

1. $24 \div 8 \times \boxed{} = 27$
2. $3 \times 3 \times 9 = \boxed{}$
3. $\boxed{} = 99 \div 9 + 53$
4. $42 \div 6 + 34 = \boxed{}$
5. $7 \times 6 - 7 = \boxed{}$
6. $\boxed{} = 11 \times 8 - 14$
7. $44 = 47 - 8 + \boxed{}$
8. $54 = 24 + \boxed{} + 22$
9. $\boxed{} = 120 \div 10 \times 8$
10. $56 \div 8 \times 6 = \boxed{}$

	Ex 35	Ex 36
1	3	28
2	6	8
3	3	6
4	66	45
5	63	5
6	5	24
7	54	28
8	4	35
9	5	32
10	54	63

Exercise A35

1. $\boxed{} = 18 + 3 \div 7$
2. $96 \div 8 \div 2 = \boxed{}$
3. $72 = \boxed{} \times 4 \times 6$
4. $8 \times 9 - 6 = \boxed{}$
5. $33 + 41 - 11 = \boxed{}$
6. $38 - 9 + \boxed{} = 34$
7. $\boxed{} = 24 \div 4 \times 9$
8. $3 = 108 \div 9 \div \boxed{}$
9. $46 = 38 + \boxed{} + 3$
10. $48 \div 6 + 46 = \boxed{}$

Exercise A36

1. $\boxed{} = 4 \times 9 - 8$
2. $22 - 11 \times \boxed{} = 88$
3. $59 = \boxed{} + 21 + 32$
4. $36 + 14 - 5 = \boxed{}$
5. $5 \times 7 \div \boxed{} = 7$
6. $\boxed{} = 48 \div 6 \times 3$
7. $45 \div 5 + \boxed{} = 37$
8. $\boxed{} = 48 \div 8 + 29$
9. $\boxed{} = 8 \times 5 - 8$
10. $24 - 15 \times 7 = \boxed{}$

Exercise A37

1. $32 + 21 - 8 = \boxed{}$
2. $55 - 10 + \boxed{} = 59$
3. $\boxed{} = 4 \times 10 - 6$
4. $\boxed{} = 19 - 11 \times 9$
5. $54 + 23 - 12 = \boxed{}$
6. $32 \div 4 - \boxed{} = 3$
7. $\boxed{} = 22 + 42 \div 8$
8. $78 = 74 - 12 + \boxed{}$
9. $60 - 4 \div \boxed{} = 8$
10. $80 \div 8 - 5 = \boxed{}$

Exercise A38

1. $3 = 81 \div 9 \div \boxed{}$
2. $\boxed{} = 9 \times 4 \div 6$
3. $6 \times 5 + 9 = \boxed{}$
4. $\boxed{} = 17 + 13 \times 3$
5. $7 \times 8 \div \boxed{} = 8$
6. $7 = 75 - 5 \div \boxed{}$
7. $8 \times 9 - \boxed{} = 57$
8. $\boxed{} = 31 - 6 \div 5$
9. $69 - 13 \div 8 = \boxed{}$
10. $50 - 10 \div \boxed{} = 8$

	Ex 37	Ex 38
1	45	3
2	14	6
3	34	39
4	72	90
5	65	7
6	5	10
7	8	15
8	16	5
9	7	7
10	5	5

Exercise A39

1. $26 - 14 \times \boxed{} = 108$
2. $\boxed{} = 7 \times 6 + 15$
3. $35 - 8 + \boxed{} = 30$
4. $\boxed{} = 38 + 6 - 2$
5. $7 \times 7 - 6 = \boxed{}$
6. $\boxed{} = 35 + 22 + 4$
7. $24 \div 4 + \boxed{} = 32$
8. $18 \div 9 + 49 = \boxed{}$
9. $\boxed{} = 46 - 8 + 6$
10. $73 - 10 \div 7 = \boxed{}$

Exercise A40

1. $17 \times 2 + \boxed{} = 59$
2. $7 + 21 + 7 = \boxed{}$
3. $\boxed{} = 49 \div 7 + 38$
4. $26 + 34 \div \boxed{} = 10$
5. $12 = 14 \div 7 \times \boxed{}$
6. $\boxed{} = 7 \times 6 - 7$
7. $6 \times 11 - 8 = \boxed{}$
8. $\boxed{} = 48 \div 6 \div 2$
9. $7 \times 6 - \boxed{} = 36$
10. $\boxed{} = 86 - 11 - 15$

	Ex 39	Ex 40
1	9	25
2	57	35
3	3	45
4	42	6
5	43	6
6	61	35
7	26	58
8	51	4
9	44	6
10	9	60

Section B

Answer Column

Exercise B1

1. $\boxed{} = 39 - 6 - 6 + 7$
2. $41 - 8 - 3 - 4 = \boxed{}$
3. $\boxed{} = 30 \div 5 \times 7 \div 6$
4. $40 \div 4 \div 5 \times \boxed{} = 20$
5. $42 - \boxed{} = 28 + 8$
6. $9 = 28 + 4 + 4 \div \boxed{}$
7. $26 + \boxed{} = 41 - 8$
8. $27 = 8 \times 5 - 8 - \boxed{}$
9. $38 - 9 + 5 - 8 = \boxed{}$
10. $\boxed{} = 23 + 5 \div 4 + 14$

Exercise B2

1. $\boxed{} = 6 \times 6 \div 6 \times 4$
2. $8 \times 6 = \boxed{} \times 4$
3. $26 + 9 \div 5 + 23 = \boxed{}$
4. $42 \div 6 = \boxed{} \div 5$
5. $6 \times \boxed{} = 44 - 8$
6. $7 \times 6 - 7 - \boxed{} = 32$
7. $35 = 44 - 10 - 7 + \boxed{}$
8. $\boxed{} + 6 = 20 + 8$
9. $4 \times 3 \times 6 \div \boxed{} = 12$
10. $\boxed{} = 24 \div 4 \times 9 \div 6$

	Ex 1	Ex 2
1	34	24
2	26	12
3	7	30
4	10	35
5	6	6
6	4	3
7	7	8
8	5	22
9	26	6
10	21	9

	Ex 3	Ex 4
1	21	8
2	26	12
3	5	5
4	34	39
5	4	6
6	4	6
7	6	4
8	4	30
9	4	5
10	8	33

Exercise B3

1. $17 + 7 = 3 + \square$
2. $\square = 32 \div 4 \div 4 + 24$
3. $4 \times 10 = \square \times 8$
4. $\square = 2 \times 4 \times 5 - 6$
5. $28 + 6 - 8 + \square = 30$
6. $3 \times \square = 60 \div 5$
7. $48 \div \square = 2 \times 4$
8. $34 = 36 - 7 + 9 - \square$
9. $36 \div \square = 54 \div 6$
10. $48 \div 6 + 24 \div 4 = \square$

Exercise B4

1. $38 - 6 = 4 \times \square$
2. $32 \div 4 \div 4 \times 6 = \square$
3. $8 + 21 + 4 - \square = 28$
4. $34 - 4 = \square - 9$
5. $42 - 9 - 2 - \square = 25$
6. $60 \div 10 = 36 \div \square$
7. $22 + \square = 3 + 23$
8. $100 \div 10 \div 5 + 28 = \square$
9. $45 - 10 = 40 - \square$
10. $\square = 2 \times 5 \times 4 - 7$

	Ex 5	Ex 6
1	7	32
2	27	21
3	3	7
4	30	80
5	3	7
6	24	4
7	4	31
8	6	10
9	20	27
10	5	4

Exercise B5

1. $5 + 23 = \square \times 4$
2. $\square = 27 + 7 - 10 + 3$
3. $43 - \square = 4 \times 10$
4. $\square = 5 \times 5 + 7 - 2$
5. $44 - 8 = 39 - \square$
6. $\square = 21 + 7 \div 4 + 17$
7. $38 - \square = 25 + 9$
8. $34 = 30 - 7 + 5 + \square$
9. $22 + 4 = \square + 6$
10. $23 + 7 - 8 + \square = 27$

Exercise B6

1. $40 \div 5 = \square \div 4$
2. $27 = 9 \times 4 \div 6 + \square$
3. $42 \div 6 + 22 + \square = 36$
4. $2 \times 4 = \square \div 10$
5. $\square = 45 \div 5 + 26 \div 5$
6. $4 \times 9 - 8 \div \square = 7$
7. $\square = 7 \times 6 - 6 - 5$
8. $54 \div 6 \times 5 - \square = 35$
9. $\square = 44 - 4 - 5 - 8$
10. $8 \times 6 = \square \times 12$

	Ex 7	Ex 8
1	7	8
2	4	31
3	9	10
4	28	25
5	28	5
6	5	12
7	21	4
8	28	6
9	32	12
10	7	42

Exercise B7

1. $31 = 6 \times 7 - 4 - \square$
2. $35 - 8 + 3 - \square = 26$
3. $28 + 7 = 26 + \square$
4. $\square = 33 - 6 + 9 - 8$
5. $4 \times 10 - 6 - 6 = \square$
6. $\square + 24 = 37 - 8$
7. $12 \div 3 - 2 + 19 = \square$
8. $\square = 24 + 6 \div 5 + 22$
9. $32 \div 4 - 5 + 29 = \square$
10. $30 \div 6 = 35 \div \square$

Exercise B8

1. $28 + \square = 4 \times 9$
2. $7 + 16 + 3 + 5 = \square$
3. $5 \times 4 = 2 \times \square$
4. $4 + 26 \div 6 \times 5 = \square$
5. $\square = 40 \div 4 \times 5 \div 10$
6. $60 = 31 - 6 \div 5 \times \square$
7. $36 \div 6 = 24 \div \square$
8. $37 - \square = 34 - 3$
9. $5 \times 4 \div 10 \times 6 = \square$
10. $\square = 72 \div 6 - 5 \times 6$

Exercise B9

1. $50 - 2 - 9 + 7 = \boxed{}$
2. $55 - 4 = \boxed{} - 2$
3. $\boxed{} = 2 \times 6 \times 6 \div 6$
4. $36 \div 6 = 42 \div \boxed{}$
5. $25 + 5 = 4 + \boxed{}$
6. $38 + 5 + 2 \div 5 = \boxed{}$
7. $59 - 8 - 4 - 7 = \boxed{}$
8. $47 - \boxed{} = 6 \times 7$
9. $31 = 43 - 6 - 8 + \boxed{}$
10. $7 + 34 = 50 - \boxed{}$

Exercise B10

1. $84 \div 7 = 6 \times \boxed{}$
2. $50 \div 5 \div 5 \times 7 = \boxed{}$
3. $\boxed{} = 21 \div 7 + 37 \div 5$
4. $42 \div 6 = 35 \div \boxed{}$
5. $57 - 7 = 5 \times \boxed{}$
6. $36 = 53 - 7 - 6 - \boxed{}$
7. $36 + 8 - 5 + 6 = \boxed{}$
8. $55 - 9 = 38 + \boxed{}$
9. $\boxed{} = 5 \times 7 \div 5 \times 6$
10. $8 \times 5 = \boxed{} \times 10$

Exercise B11

1. $35 + 7 \div 7 + 24 = \boxed{}$
2. $\boxed{} \div 5 = 28 \div 7$
3. $25 = 48 \div 4 \div 4 + \boxed{}$
4. $\boxed{} = 2 \times 4 \times 5 - 2$
5. $41 = 32 + 8 + 6 - \boxed{}$
6. $29 + \boxed{} = 8 + 27$
7. $5 \times 2 \times 7 \div \boxed{} = 7$
8. $8 = 40 \div 5 \times 6 \div \boxed{}$
9. $6 \times \boxed{} = 54 - 6$
10. $50 \div 5 \div 5 + 39 = \boxed{}$

Exercise B12

1. $57 - 9 - 8 - \boxed{} = 37$
2. $\boxed{} = 53 - 6 - 3 - 8$
3. $31 + 9 - 2 + \boxed{} = 43$
4. $\boxed{} = 41 - 7 + 4 + 1$
5. $54 \div 6 \times 7 \div \boxed{} = 9$
6. $7 \times 8 = \boxed{} \times 7$
7. $39 + \boxed{} = 9 + 37$
8. $\boxed{} = 39 + 9 \div 6 + 33$
9. $5 \times \boxed{} = 60 - 5$
10. $6 \times 7 - 2 - \boxed{} = 34$

Exercise B13

1. $11 \times \boxed{} = 59 - 4$
2. $38 + 6 - \boxed{} - 8 = 34$
3. $34 = 2 + 6 + 32 - \boxed{}$
4. $8 \times 6 = 39 + \boxed{}$
5. $51 - \boxed{} - 7 - 2 = 38$
6. $36 \div 6 + 37 - \boxed{} = 37$
7. $\boxed{} \div 5 = 28 \div 7$
8. $56 - 3 = 58 - \boxed{}$
9. $\boxed{} = 36 + 9 - 5 \div 10$
10. $60 - 4 \div 7 + 22 = \boxed{}$

Exercise B14

1. $45 \div 5 = 54 \div \boxed{}$
2. $\boxed{} = 48 \div 6 \times 5 + 5$
3. $6 \times 5 \div 5 + 24 = \boxed{}$
4. $3 + \boxed{} = 4 \times 6$
5. $47 = 4 + 4 \times 4 + \boxed{}$
6. $\boxed{} = 12 \times 10 \div 10 \div 6$
7. $70 \div 7 = 2 \times \boxed{}$
8. $54 - \boxed{} = 9 \times 5$
9. $8 \times 7 - 8 - \boxed{} = 41$
10. $63 \div 7 - 4 \times 6 = \boxed{}$

	Ex 9	Ex 10
1	46	2
2	53	14
3	12	8
4	7	5
5	26	10
6	9	4
7	40	45
8	5	8
9	2	42
10	9	4

	Ex 11	Ex 12
1	30	3
2	20	36
3	22	5
4	38	39
5	5	7
6	6	8
7	10	7
8	6	41
9	8	11
10	41	6

	Ex 13	Ex 14
1	5	6
2	2	45
3	6	30
4	9	21
5	4	15
6	6	2
7	20	5
8	5	9
9	4	7
10	30	30

	Ex 15	Ex 16
1	8	6
2	41	5
3	7	7
4	37	2
5	39	60
6	2	44
7	46	6
8	30	3
9	8	4
10	5	56

Exercise B15

1. $54 - 7 = \square + 39$
2. $\square = 32 + 8 - 5 + 6$
3. $27 + 6 = 40 - \square$
4. $44 - 4 - 8 + 5 = \square$
5. $\square = 7 \times 7 - 6 - 4$
6. $46 - 8 + 6 - \square = 42$
7. $39 + 2 = \square - 5$
8. $36 + 6 \div 6 + 23 = \square$
9. $26 + \square = 42 - 8$
10. $\square = 58 - 3 - 5 \div 10$

Exercise B16

1. $7 \times 4 = \square + 22$
2. $3 + 6 \times 5 \div \square = 9$
3. $\square = 5 \times 7 + 7 \div 6$
4. $6 \times \square = 60 \div 5$
5. $10 \times 7 \div 7 \times 6 = \square$
6. $\square - 2 = 50 - 8$
7. $36 = 12 \times 5 \div 10 \times \square$
8. $\square = 5 \times 8 - 10 \div 10$
9. $8 \times 7 = 60 - \square$
10. $50 - 10 \div 5 \times 7 = \square$

	Ex 17	Ex 18
1	6	12
2	24	7
3	7	61
4	18	7
5	4	6
6	51	50
7	9	7
8	43	5
9	62	8
10	8	2

Exercise B17

1. $54 = 55 - 7 + 12 - \square$
2. $64 - 9 = 31 + \square$
3. $80 \div 8 = 70 \div \square$
4. $\square = 72 \div 9 \div 4 \times 9$
5. $63 \div 7 + 23 \div 8 = \square$
6. $\square = 96 \div 8 + 33 + 6$
7. $61 = 2 \times 5 \times 7 - \square$
8. $\square = 7 \times 8 - 5 - 8$
9. $\square = 25 + 41 + 4 - 8$
10. $27 + \square = 23 + 12$

Exercise B18

1. $2 \times 3 \times 8 \div 4 = \square$
2. $9 \times 7 = \square \times 9$
3. $\square = 25 + 24 \div 7 + 54$
4. $8 = 22 + 31 + 3 \div \square$
5. $15 - 7 \times 8 - \square = 58$
6. $5 \times 8 = \square - 10$
7. $36 + 22 + 6 - \square = 57$
8. $65 = 31 + 8 + 31 - \square$
9. $10 \times 9 \div 10 \times \square = 72$
10. $\square = 14 \times 2 \div 7 \div 2$

	Ex 19	Ex 20
1	5	2
2	4	2
3	9	5
4	7	9
5	12	11
6	61	2
7	8	21
8	3	8
9	24	52
10	2	7

Exercise B19

1. $40 \div 5 = 3 + \square$
2. $24 \div \square = 42 \div 7$
3. $51 - \square = 6 \times 7$
4. $23 = 24 - 9 \times 2 - \square$
5. $62 - 5 - 7 + \square = 62$
6. $\square = 33 + 26 - 6 + 8$
7. $12 = 2 \times 6 \times 8 \div \square$
8. $3 \times \square = 81 \div 9$
9. $33 + 15 = \square + 24$
10. $84 \div 7 \div 3 \div 2 = \square$

Exercise B20

1. $\square \times 14 = 4 \times 7$
2. $26 = 26 - 6 - 7 \times \square$
3. $56 - \square = 43 + 8$
4. $67 - 10 + 5 - \square = 53$
5. $88 \div 8 \times 7 \div 7 = \square$
6. $64 \div 8 = 4 \times \square$
7. $\square + 34 = 43 + 12$
8. $16 + 32 + 8 \div \square = 7$
9. $53 - 9 = \square - 8$
10. $2 \times 5 \times 7 - \square = 63$

ONE-A-WEEK – *Mental Arithmetic Tests Book 3*
© Folens

Exercise B21

1. $11 \times 7 = \boxed{} \times 11$
2. $54 = 51 - 4 + 12 - \boxed{}$
3. $32 + 26 - 3 + \boxed{} = 60$
4. $27 + 32 - 8 - 4 = \boxed{}$
5. $\boxed{} \times 8 = 75 - 3$
6. $24 \div 8 = 21 \div \boxed{}$
7. $\boxed{} = 66 - 8 + 2 \div 6$
8. $99 \div 9 + 52 - 4 = \boxed{}$
9. $21 + \boxed{} = 68 - 6$
10. $58 = 3 + 48 - 6 + \boxed{}$

Exercise B22

1. $5 \times \boxed{} = 70 \div 7$
2. $27 + 8 = 25 + \boxed{}$
3. $56 \div 7 = \boxed{} \div 6$
4. $\boxed{} = 9 \div 3 \times 8 \div 2$
5. $7 = 31 + 24 + 8 \div \boxed{}$
6. $57 - 5 = 58 - \boxed{}$
7. $48 \div 6 = \boxed{} \times 2$
8. $\boxed{} = 7 \times 8 - 6 \times 3$
9. $6 \times 12 - 5 - \boxed{} = 60$
10. $54 = 72 \div 6 - 3 \times \boxed{}$

	Ex 21	Ex 22
1	7	2
2	5	10
3	5	48
4	47	12
5	9	9
6	7	6
7	10	4
8	59	150
9	41	7
10	13	6

Exercise B23

1. $\boxed{} = 58 - 7 + 11 - 6$
2. $19 = 11 + 3 \times 2 - \boxed{}$
3. $45 + 14 = 66 - \boxed{}$
4. $8 \times 4 = \boxed{} + 20$
5. $200 = 6 \times 9 - 4 \times \boxed{}$
6. $\boxed{} = 24 + 21 \div 5 + 41$
7. $29 = 80 \div 10 - \boxed{} + 26$
8. $70 - \boxed{} = 73 - 9$
9. $67 - 8 + 5 \div 8 = \boxed{}$
10. $41 + 13 = \boxed{} + 22$

Exercise B24

1. $12 + 37 + 5 \div \boxed{} = 9$
2. $\boxed{} = 8 \times 6 \div 4 \times 8$
3. $10 \times 6 \div 5 \div 3 = \boxed{}$
4. $35 \div 7 + 24 + \boxed{} = 60$
5. $6 \times \boxed{} = 3 \times 12$
6. $9 \times 4 = \boxed{} \times 3$
7. $2 \times 3 \times 5 \div 10 = \boxed{}$
8. $50 - 10 - 10 \times \boxed{} = 120$
9. $\boxed{} = 4 \times 6 \div 8 \times 9$
10. $73 - \boxed{} = 11 \times 6$

	Ex 23	Ex 24
1	56	6
2	9	96
3	7	4
4	12	31
5	4	6
6	50	12
7	5	3
8	6	4
9	8	27
10	32	7

Exercise B25

1. $90 - 12 - 15 + 9 = \boxed{}$
2. $24 - 13 \times 8 - \boxed{} = 76$
3. $99 \div 11 \times 4 \div 3 = \boxed{}$
4. $36 \div 4 = 63 \div \boxed{}$
5. $\boxed{} = 71 - 15 + 13 - 14$
6. $28 + 12 \div 10 + \boxed{} = 67$
7. $66 = 84 - 14 - 11 + \boxed{}$
8. $83 - 14 = 79 - \boxed{}$
9. $2 = 31 + 33 \div 8 \div \boxed{}$
10. $34 + 44 = 89 - \boxed{}$

Exercise B26

1. $\boxed{} \times 9 = 9 \times 5$
2. $6 \times \boxed{} = 96 \div 8$
3. $49 \div \boxed{} = 63 \div 9$
4. $\boxed{} = 13 + 53 + 6 \div 9$
5. $\boxed{} = 4 \times 4 \times 2 - 12$
6. $57 = 9 \times 9 - 11 - \boxed{}$
7. $71 - 13 - 10 + 21 = \boxed{}$
8. $\boxed{} = 23 + 46 + 5 - 12$
9. $56 \div 7 = \boxed{} \div 9$
10. $\boxed{} = 10 \times 7 \div 10 \times 8$

	Ex 25	Ex 26
1	72	5
2	12	2
3	12	7
4	7	8
5	55	20
6	63	13
7	7	69
8	10	62
9	4	72
10	11	56

	Ex 27	Ex 28
1	8	14
2	78	40
3	13	64
4	9	12
5	13	28
6	44	7
7	8	21
8	27	8
9	24	8
10	9	4

Exercise B27

1. $70 \div 7 = 80 \div \square$
2. $88 \div 8 + 43 + 24 = \square$
3. $\square = 27 - 13 \times 2 - 15$
4. $4 \times \square = 6 \times 6$
5. $83 - \square = 51 + 19$
6. $42 + 26 = 24 + \square$
7. $7 = 4 \times 2 \times 7 \div \square$
8. $\square = 108 \div 9 \div 4 \times 9$
9. $32 + 43 = 51 + \square$
10. $\square = 31 + 17 + 6 \div 6$

Exercise B28

1. $8 \times 9 = 86 - \square$
2. $32 - 11 - 13 \times 5 = \square$
3. $\square = 63 + 9 - 14 + 6$
4. $74 - \square = 77 - 15$
5. $84 \div 7 \div 3 \times 7 = \square$
6. $8 \times 9 \div 8 \times \square = 63$
7. $46 + \square = 54 + 13$
8. $4 = 77 \div 7 + 21 \div \square$
9. $78 - 14 = \square \times 8$
10. $73 - 12 - 11 \times \square = 200$

	Ex 29	Ex 30
1	64	4
2	21	8
3	10	21
4	14	6
5	12	2
6	8	6
7	11	2
8	70	7
9	43	63
10	3	14

Exercise B29

1. $10 \times 9 - 12 - 14 = \square$
2. $\square = 29 - 11 \times 2 - 15$
3. $69 = 2 \times 19 + 41 - \square$
4. $55 + \square = 32 + 37$
5. $9 \times 8 = 84 - \square$
6. $28 \div 4 = 56 \div \square$
7. $68 - \square = 71 - 14$
8. $\square = 90 \div 10 + 72 - 11$
9. $26 + 51 = 34 + \square$
10. $3 = 22 + 23 \div 5 \div \square$

Exercise B30

1. $34 + 14 \div 6 \times \square = 32$
2. $40 \div \square = 45 \div 9$
3. $5 \times 7 \div 5 \times 3 = \square$
4. $9 \times 2 = \square + 12$
5. $\square \times 18 = 12 \times 3$
6. $2 \times 6 = 72 \div \square$
7. $5 \times 6 \div 3 \div 5 = \square$
8. $21 \div \square = 27 \div 9$
9. $\square = 96 \div 8 - 3 \times 7$
10. $78 - 11 = 81 - \square$

	Ex 31	Ex 32
1	64	13
2	180	9
3	31	5
4	7	99
5	64	3
6	7	6
7	15	10
8	14	8
9	69	5
10	12	10

Exercise B31

1. $\square = 73 - 11 + 15 - 13$
2. $7 + 61 - 8 \times 3 = \square$
3. $83 - 11 = \square + 41$
4. $22 + 20 = 6 \times \square$
5. $85 - 14 + 5 - 12 = \square$
6. $23 + 51 - 11 \div \square = 9$
7. $65 = 88 - 13 + 5 - \square$
8. $41 + 15 + 32 - \square = 74$
9. $72 - 12 + 19 - 10 = \square$
10. $77 - \square = 35 + 30$

Exercise B32

1. $76 = 81 \div 9 \times 7 + \square$
2. $42 \div 6 = 63 \div \square$
3. $\square = 8 \times 3 + 11 \div 7$
4. $25 + 52 \div 7 \times 9 = \square$
5. $\square = 54 \div 6 + 12 \div 7$
6. $67 - 13 = \square \times 9$
7. $11 \times 8 - 8 \div \square = 8$
8. $\square = 16 \div 8 \times 16 \div 4$
9. $35 \div 7 \times 9 \div \square = 9$
10. $\square = 12 \times 7 - 14 \div 7$

Exercise B33

1. 34 - 4 = 39 - ☐
2. 83 - ☐ = 51 + 19
3. 42 ÷ 7 = 36 ÷ ☐
4. 9 x ☐ = 5 x 9
5. 50 ÷ 5 ÷ 2 + ☐ = 72
6. 35 ÷ ☐ = 42 ÷ 6
7. 20 = 4 x 4 x 2 - ☐
8. 6 x 7 - 2 - ☐ = 34
9. 32 + 8 + 6 - 5 = ☐
10. 34 + 44 = ☐ - 11

Exercise B34

1. 40 ÷ 4 ÷ 5 x ☐ = 20
2. 72 ÷ 9 ÷ 4 x 9 = ☐
3. ☐ = 22 + 3 + 31 ÷ 7
4. 3 + 21 = ☐ + 7
5. ☐ = 8 x 5 - 8 - 5
6. 52 - ☐ = 53 - 9
7. ☐ = 62 - 5 - 7 + 12
8. 54 = 55 - 7 + 12 - ☐
9. 2 x 3 x 8 ÷ ☐ = 12
10. ☐ x 6 = 96 ÷ 8

	Ex 33	Ex 34
1	9	10
2	13	18
3	6	8
4	5	17
5	67	27
6	5	8
7	12	62
8	6	6
9	41	4
10	89	2

Exercise B35

1. 24 + ☐ = 15 + 33
2. 63 ÷ 7 + 23 ÷ 8 = ☐
3. 4 x 7 = 14 x ☐
4. 59 - ☐ - 4 - 7 = 40
5. ☐ = 90 - 15 - 12 + 9
6. 38 - 9 + 5 - ☐ = 26
7. 9 = 54 ÷ 6 x 7 ÷ ☐
8. ☐ = 10 x 9 ÷ 10 x 8
9. ☐ = 23 + 5 ÷ 4 + 14
10. 28 + 12 ÷ 10 + ☐ = 67

Exercise B36

1. 64 - 6 - ☐ - 12 = 38
2. 7 x 6 = 51 - ☐
3. ☐ + 23 = 8 + 27
4. 36 + 8 - 5 + 6 = ☐
5. 60 ÷ 5 = ☐ x 4
6. ☐ = 99 ÷ 11 x 4 ÷ 3
7. 63 ÷ ☐ = 49 ÷ 7
8. ☐ = 50 ÷ 5 ÷ 5 + 39
9. 78 - 14 = ☐ x 8
10. ☐ = 2 x 5 x 4 - 7

	Ex 35	Ex 36
1	24	8
2	4	9
3	2	12
4	8	45
5	72	3
6	8	12
7	7	9
8	72	41
9	21	8
10	63	33

Exercise B37

1. 10 x 9 - 14 - 12 = ☐
2. ☐ = 2 x 19 + 41 - 10
3. 27 = 27 + 7 - 10 + ☐
4. 54 = 51 - 4 + 12 - ☐
5. ☐ = 21 + 24 ÷ 5 + 41
6. 56 ÷ 8 = 28 ÷ ☐
7. 6 + ☐ = 4 + 22
8. ☐ = 36 + 6 ÷ 6 + 23
9. 80 ÷ 10 - 5 + 26 = ☐
10. 80 - 12 = 78 - ☐

Exercise B38

1. 4 x 10 = 5 x ☐
2. 23 + 9 ÷ 8 x 6 = ☐
3. ☐ = 40 ÷ 4 x 5 ÷ 10
4. 32 ÷ 4 = ☐ ÷ 5
5. ☐ = 6 x 5 ÷ 5 + 24
6. 58 - ☐ = 57 - 5
7. 12 x 5 ÷ 10 x 6 = ☐
8. ☐ = 63 ÷ 7 - 4 x 6
9. 11 x 8 - 8 ÷ ☐ = 8
10. ☐ = 7 x 6 - 6 - 5

	Ex 37	Ex 38
1	64	8
2	69	24
3	3	5
4	5	40
5	50	30
6	4	6
7	20	36
8	30	30
9	29	10
10	10	31

	Ex 39	Ex 40
1	28	13
2	12	2
3	59	4
4	6	6
5	4	14
6	2	7
7	13	20
8	13	6
9	35	9
10	32	9

Exercise B39

1. $26 + 9 = \boxed{} + 7$
2. $20 + \boxed{} = 4 \times 8$
3. $\boxed{} - 4 = 5 \times 11$
4. $58 - 7 + 11 - \boxed{} = 56$
5. $39 = 7 \times 7 - 6 - \boxed{}$
6. $46 - 5 = \boxed{} + 39$
7. $69 = 52 - 7 + 11 + \boxed{}$
8. $48 + 3 - 6 + \boxed{} = 58$
9. $30 + \boxed{} = 77 - 12$
10. $32 \div 4 - 5 + 29 = \boxed{}$

Exercise B40

1. $108 \div 9 + 24 + \boxed{} = 49$
2. $6 \times \boxed{} = 60 \div 5$
3. $\boxed{} = 24 \div 8 + 17 \div 5$
4. $31 + 41 = 12 \times \boxed{}$
5. $21 + 22 + \boxed{} + 3 = 60$
6. $49 \div 7 \times 8 - \boxed{} = 49$
7. $\boxed{} = 52 - 8 - 10 - 14$
8. $12 \times 4 = \boxed{} \times 8$
9. $45 = 65 - 15 \div 10 \times \boxed{}$
10. $27 \div \boxed{} = 21 \div 7$

Answer Column

Section C

	Ex 1	Ex 2
1	4	45
2	12	5
3	3	26
4	2	4
5	14	27
6	21	4
7	3	6
8	5	21
9	22	2
10	2	36

Exercise C1

1. $42 - 2 - \boxed{} = 28 + 8$
2. $35 = 44 - 10 - 7 - 4 + \boxed{}$
3. $8 \times 6 \div 4 = \boxed{} \times 4$
4. $4 \times 3 \times 6 \div 6 \times \boxed{} = 24$
5. $42 \div 6 + 21 = \boxed{} + 14$
6. $12 + 7 + 5 = 3 + \boxed{}$
7. $7 \times 6 - 4 - 3 - \boxed{} = 32$
8. $4 \times 5 \times 2 = \boxed{} \times 8$
9. $\boxed{} + 6 = 15 + 8 + 5$
10. $2 + 28 + 6 - 8 + \boxed{} = 30$

Exercise C2

1. $\boxed{} = 24 \div 4 \times 9 \div 6 \times 5$
2. $48 \div 6 \times \boxed{} = 10 \times 4$
3. $\boxed{} = 32 \div 4 \div 4 + 16 + 8$
4. $36 \div \boxed{} = 24 \div 6 + 5$
5. $\boxed{} = 2 \times 4 \times 5 - 6 - 7$
6. $38 - 6 = 4 \times 2 \times \boxed{}$
7. $34 = 36 - 7 + 3 - 4 + \boxed{}$
8. $8 + 21 + 4 - 5 + \boxed{} = 49$
9. $3 \times \boxed{} = 60 \div 5 \div 2$
10. $32 \div 4 \div 4 \times 6 \times 3 = \boxed{}$

	Ex 3	Ex 4
1	39	29
2	5	21
3	8	7
4	7	38
5	39	3
6	29	12
7	12	4
8	28	6
9	10	4
10	21	30

Exercise C3

1. $48 \div 6 + 24 \div 4 + 31 = \boxed{}$
2. $17 + \boxed{} + 4 = 3 + 23$
3. $42 - 9 - 2 - 6 - \boxed{} = 17$
4. $45 - 10 - 6 = 36 - \boxed{}$
5. $39 - 4 - 5 = \boxed{} - 9$
6. $\boxed{} = 39 - 6 - 6 + 7 - 5$
7. $60 \div 10 \times 6 = 3 \times \boxed{}$
8. $\boxed{} = 30 \div 5 \times 7 \div 6 \times 4$
9. $100 \div 10 \div 5 + 28 \div 3 = \boxed{}$
10. $\boxed{} = 11 + 12 + 5 \div 4 + 14$

Exercise C4

1. $\boxed{} = 2 \times 5 \times 4 - 7 - 4$
2. $41 - 8 - 3 - 4 - 5 = \boxed{}$
3. $26 + \boxed{} = 41 - 5 - 3$
4. $38 - 9 + 5 - 8 + 12 = \boxed{}$
5. $40 \div 4 \div 5 \times 6 \div \boxed{} = 4$
6. $\boxed{} = 6 \times 6 \div 6 \times 4 \div 2$
7. $9 = 13 + 15 + 4 + 4 \div \boxed{}$
8. $6 \times \boxed{} = 49 - 8 - 5$
9. $21 = 8 \times 5 - 8 - 7 - \boxed{}$
10. $26 + 9 \div 5 + 10 + 13 = \boxed{}$

Exercise C5

1. ☐ = 5 x 4 + 7 - 2 + 5
2. 44 - 8 = 46 - 7 - ☐
3. 31 = 6 x 7 - 4 - 10 + ☐
4. 35 - 8 + 3 - 20 + ☐ = 26
5. 12 + 16 + 7 = 26 + ☐
6. 22 ÷ 2 + 15 = ☐ + 6
7. 12 + 7 + 11 - 8 + ☐ = 27
8. ☐ + 24 = 33 - 8 + 4
9. 12 ÷ 3 - 2 + 12 + 7 = ☐
10. ☐ = 24 + 6 ÷ 5 + 22 + 5

Exercise C6

1. 2 x 2 x 2 = ☐ ÷ 10
2. ☐ = 45 ÷ 5 + 26 ÷ 5 x 6
3. 28 + ☐ = 3 x 4 x 3
4. 7 + 16 + 3 + 5 + 7 = ☐
5. 5 x 4 = 2 x 5 x ☐
6. ☐ = 44 - 4 - 5 - 8 ÷ 3
7. 8 x 6 = ☐ x 3 x 8
8. 60 = 31 - 6 ÷ 5 x 4 x ☐
9. 42 ÷ 6 - ☐ = 24 ÷ 4
10. 37 - ☐ = 44 - 8 - 8

Exercise C7

1. ☐ = 33 - 6 + 9 - 8 + 21
2. 4 x 10 - 6 - 6 + 11 = ☐
3. 11 + 23 = ☐ x 4 + 6
4. ☐ = 27 + 7 - 10 + 3 + 21
5. 30 - 5 + ☐ = 4 x 10
6. 32 ÷ 4 - 5 + 29 - 3 = ☐
7. 30 ÷ 6 = 40 ÷ ☐ + 1
8. ☐ = 21 + 7 ÷ 4 + 17 + 13
9. 38 - ☐ = 25 + 13 - 4
10. 34 + 2 = 30 - 7 + 5 + ☐

Exercise C8

1. 4 + 26 ÷ 6 x 5 + 14 = ☐
2. ☐ = 40 ÷ 4 x 5 ÷ 10 x 6
3. 40 ÷ 5 = 21 + 11 ÷ ☐
4. 27 = 9 x 4 ÷ 6 + 7 + ☐
5. 6 x 7 ÷ 6 + 22 + ☐ = 36
6. 5 x 4 ÷ 10 x 6 x 4 = ☐
7. ☐ = 72 ÷ 6 - 5 x 6 - 7
8. 4 x 9 - 8 ÷ 4 x ☐ = 70
9. ☐ = 21 ÷ 3 x 6 - 6 - 5
10. 54 ÷ 6 x 5 - 8 - ☐ = 33

Exercise C9

1. 7 + 21 + 13 = 50 - ☐
2. 29 + 8 - 5 + 6 + 7 = ☐
3. 50 ÷ 5 ÷ 5 x 7 ÷ 7 = ☐
4. ☐ = 5 x 7 ÷ 5 x 6 ÷ 7
5. 42 ÷ 6 + 21 = 15 + ☐
6. 35 + 7 ÷ 7 + 24 ÷ 10 = ☐
7. 60 = 40 - 7 - 6 - 7 x ☐
8. 6 x ☐ = 58 - 6 - 4
9. ☐ - 9 = 28 + 8 + 10
10. 49 = 32 + 8 + 6 + 8 - ☐

Exercise C10

1. 84 ÷ 7 = 2 x 2 x ☐
2. 5 x 2 x 7 ÷ 10 x ☐ = 35
3. ☐ ÷ 5 + 8 = 84 ÷ 7
4. 25 = 48 ÷ 4 ÷ 4 + 13 + ☐
5. ☐ = 2 x 4 x 5 - 2 - 9
6. 57 - 9 - 8 - 10 x ☐ = 90
7. 29 - 3 + ☐ = 8 + 27
8. 31 + 9 - 5 + 3 + ☐ = 43
9. 36 = 40 ÷ 5 x 6 ÷ 4 x ☐
10. 54 ÷ 6 ÷ 3 x 5 ÷ ☐ = 3

Answers

	Ex 5	Ex 6	Ex 7	Ex 8	Ex 9	Ex 10
1	30	80	49	39	9	3
2	3	42	39	30	45	5
3	3	8	7	4	2	20
4	16	38	48	14	6	9
5	9	2	15	7	13	29
6	20	9	29	48	3	3
7	5	2	10	35	3	9
8	5	3	37	10	8	5
9	21	1	4	31	55	3
10	33	9	8	4	5	5

Ex 11	Ex 12
1 41	8
2 7	31
3 29	5
4 5	7
5 39	12
6 36	16
7 2	25
8 60	2
9 49	5
10 26	4

Exercise C11

1. $50 \div 5 \div 5 + 20 + 19 = \boxed{}$
2. $39 + \boxed{} = 9 + 24 + 13$
3. $\boxed{} = 53 - 6 - 3 - 8 - 7$
4. $5 \times 11 - \boxed{} = 60 - 10$
5. $\boxed{} = 47 - 7 + 4 + 1 - 6$
6. $50 - 2 - 9 + 7 - 10 = \boxed{}$
7. $7 \times 8 = \boxed{} \times 4 \times 7$
8. $\boxed{} = 2 \times 6 \times 6 \div 6 \times 5$
9. $\boxed{} = 39 + 9 \div 6 + 33 + 8$
10. $25 + 14 = 4 + 9 + \boxed{}$

Exercise C12

1. $6 \times 7 - 2 - 6 - \boxed{} = 26$
2. $59 - 8 - 4 - 7 - 9 = \boxed{}$
3. $55 - 4 = 43 + 13 - \boxed{}$
4. $40 = 43 - 6 - 8 + 4 + \boxed{}$
5. $36 \div 3 \times 7 = 7 \times \boxed{}$
6. $8 \times 5 \div 10 = \boxed{} \div 4$
7. $19 + 5 + 6 \div 5 + 19 = \boxed{}$
8. $\boxed{} = 21 \div 7 + 37 \div 5 \div 4$
9. $57 - 10 - \boxed{} = 6 \times 7$
10. $57 - 7 = 9 \times 6 - \boxed{}$

Ex 13	Ex 14
1 9	11
2 49	5
3 15	8
4 41	31
5 2	21
6 4	7
7 46	90
8 6	7
9 46	6
10 6	18

Exercise C13

1. $8 \times 7 - 8 = 39 + \boxed{}$
2. $51 - 4 - 7 - 2 + 11 = \boxed{}$
3. $54 - 7 = 22 + \boxed{} + 10$
4. $\boxed{} = 4 \times 8 + 8 - 5 + 6$
5. $27 + 6 = 40 - 9 + \boxed{}$
6. $\boxed{} = 36 + 9 - 5 \div 5 - 4$
7. $60 - 4 \div 7 + 22 + 16 = \boxed{}$
8. $46 - 8 + 6 - 2 \div \boxed{} = 7$
9. $27 + 12 + 2 = \boxed{} - 5$
10. $36 + 6 \div 6 + 23 \div 5 = \boxed{}$

Exercise C14

1. $6 + 7 + \boxed{} = 4 \times 6$
2. $40 = 4 + 4 \times 7 \div 7 \times \boxed{}$
3. $7 \times 4 = 9 + 11 + \boxed{}$
4. $3 + 6 \times 5 \div 5 + \boxed{} = 40$
5. $\boxed{} = 5 \times 7 + 7 \div 6 \times 3$
6. $8 \times 7 - 8 - 6 \div \boxed{} = 6$
7. $63 \div 7 - 4 \times 6 \times 3 = \boxed{}$
8. $24 \div 4 \times \boxed{} = 50 - 8$
9. $36 = 36 \div 3 \times 5 \div 10 \times \boxed{}$
10. $\boxed{} = 5 \times 8 - 10 \div 10 \times 6$

Ex 15	Ex 16
1 46	2
2 44	10
3 4	2
4 2	2
5 4	43
6 4	3
7 33	49
8 9	14
9 20	2
10 10	8

Exercise C15

1. $44 - 4 - 8 + 5 + 9 = \boxed{}$
2. $\boxed{} = 7 \times 7 - 6 - 4 + 5$
3. $33 = 2 \times 4 + 32 - 3 - \boxed{}$
4. $38 + 6 - \boxed{} - 3 - 5 = 34$
5. $11 \times \boxed{} = 49 - 8 + 3$
6. $26 + 4 + \boxed{} = 42 - 8$
7. $\boxed{} = 58 - 3 - 5 \div 10 + 28$
8. $36 \div 6 + 37 + 3 - \boxed{} = 37$
9. $\boxed{} \div 5 = 28 \div 4 - 3$
10. $56 - 3 - 5 = 58 - \boxed{}$

Exercise C16

1. $2 \times 3 \times \boxed{} = 60 \div 5$
2. $10 \times 7 \div 7 \times 6 \div 6 = \boxed{}$
3. $45 \div 5 = 28 \div 4 + \boxed{}$
4. $\boxed{} = 48 \div 6 \times 5 \div 5 \div 4$
5. $6 \times 5 \div 5 + 24 + 13 = \boxed{}$
6. $7 \times 7 = 60 - \boxed{} - 8$
7. $50 - 10 \div 5 \times 7 - 7 = \boxed{}$
8. $\boxed{} = 12 \times 10 \div 10 \div 6 \times 7$
9. $70 \div 7 = 4 \times 5 \div \boxed{}$
10. $58 - 5 - \boxed{} = 9 \times 5$

Exercise C17

1. 37 + 6 - ☐ = 23 + 12
2. 36 + 22 + 6 - 8 - ☐ = 51
3. 9 x 7 ÷ ☐ = 3 x 3
4. 10 x 9 ÷ 10 x 4 ÷ ☐ = 6
5. 51 = 22 + 31 + 3 ÷ 7 + ☐
6. 40 ÷ 5 = 25 ÷ 5 + ☐
7. 5 x 8 = 11 x 4 - ☐
8. 51 - 5 - ☐ = 6 x 7
9. 59 = 31 + 8 + 11 - 6 + ☐
10. 51 - 5 - 7 + 21 + ☐ = 62

Exercise C18

1. ☐ = 14 x 2 ÷ 7 ÷ 2 x 8
2. 72 = 2 x 6 x 8 ÷ 8 x ☐
3. 24 ÷ 8 + ☐ = 42 ÷ 7
4. 33 + 15 = ☐ + 13 + 24
5. 51 = 24 - 9 x 2 x 2 - ☐
6. ☐ x 14 = 2 x 7 x 2
7. ☐ = 33 + 26 - 6 + 8 - 7
8. 67 - 9 - ☐ = 43 + 8
9. 3 x ☐ = 81 ÷ 9 ÷ 3
10. 88 ÷ 8 x 7 ÷ 7 x 8 = ☐

	Ex 17	Ex 18
1	8	16
2	5	6
3	7	3
4	6	11
5	43	9
6	3	2
7	4	54
8	4	7
9	15	1
10	2	88

Exercise C19

1. 84 ÷ 7 + 32 ÷ 4 + 48 = ☐
2. 7 x 8 = 70 ÷ 10 x ☐
3. 42 = 26 - 6 x 3 - 10 - ☐
4. 53 - 9 - 6 = ☐ - 8
5. 67 - 10 + 5 - 6 - ☐ = 49
6. 64 = 55 - 7 + 12 - 6 + ☐
7. 64 ÷ 8 = 4 x 4 ÷ ☐
8. ☐ + 24 + 23 = 29 + 30
9. 16 + 32 + 8 ÷ 7 ÷ ☐ = 2
10. 63 ÷ 7 + 23 ÷ 8 + 59 = ☐

Exercise C20

1. ☐ = 25 + 24 ÷ 7 + 54 + 3
2. 53 = 2 x 5 x 7 - 9 - ☐
3. 62 - 9 = 13 + 31 + ☐
4. ☐ = 13 + 12 + 41 + 4 - 8
5. ☐ = 72 ÷ 9 ÷ 4 x 9 ÷ 6
6. 2 x 3 x 8 ÷ 4 x 8 = ☐
7. ☐ = 96 ÷ 8 + 33 + 5 ÷ 10
8. 2 x 5 x 7 - 7 - ☐ = 58
9. ☐ = 7 x 8 - 5 - 8 - 6
10. 15 - 7 x 8 - 6 - ☐ = 55

	Ex 19	Ex 20
1	59	64
2	8	8
3	8	9
4	46	62
5	7	3
6	10	96
7	2	5
8	12	5
9	4	37
10	63	3

Exercise C21

1. 3 x 9 + 32 - 8 - 4 = ☐
2. ☐ x 8 = 75 - 3 - 8
3. ☐ = 58 - 7 + 11 - 6 + 5
4. 60 = 11 + 3 x 2 - 9 + ☐
5. 45 + 14 = 6 x 8 + ☐
6. 21 + 22 + ☐ = 74 - 6
7. 58 = 3 + 45 ÷ 8 + 24 + ☐
8. ☐ = 24 + 21 ÷ 5 + 41 - 7
9. 60 = 80 ÷ 10 - 5 + 26 + ☐
10. 72 ÷ 8 + ☐ = 39 - 7

Exercise C22

1. ☐ = 9 ÷ 3 x 8 ÷ 2 x 8
2. 35 = 31 + 24 + 8 ÷ 9 x ☐
3. 12 + 37 + 5 ÷ 6 x ☐ = 72
4. ☐ = 56 ÷ 7 x 6 ÷ 4 x 8
5. 10 x 6 ÷ 5 ÷ 3 x 7 = ☐
6. 6 x 12 - 5 - 7 ÷ ☐ = 12
7. 9 = 72 ÷ 6 - 3 x 6 ÷ ☐
8. 10 x 4 = 12 x 4 - ☐
9. 2 x 3 x 5 ÷ 10 x 7 = ☐
10. 50 - 10 - 10 x 4 ÷ ☐ = 12

	Ex 21	Ex 22
1	47	96
2	8	5
3	61	8
4	41	96
5	11	28
6	25	5
7	28	6
8	43	8
9	31	21
10	23	10

Ex 23	Ex 24
1 **12**	**5**
2 **50**	**31**
3 **22**	**2**
4 **8**	**12**
5 **6**	**6**
6 **2**	**22**
7 **21**	**7**
8 **7**	**8**
9 **39**	**9**
10 **52**	**50**

Exercise C23

1. $8 \times 4 = \square + 6 + 14$
2. $200 = 6 \times 9 - 4 \times 3 + \square$
3. $11 \times 5 = 3 \times 11 + \square$
4. $46 = 51 - 4 + 12 - 5 - \square$
5. $32 + 26 - 7 + 13 - \square = 58$
6. $67 - 8 + 5 \div 8 \div 4 = \square$
7. $41 + 13 = \square + 21 + 12$
8. $24 \div 8 = 8 + 13 \div \square$
9. $\square = 66 - 8 + 2 \div 6 + 29$
10. $99 \div 9 + 52 - 4 - 7 = \square$

Exercise C24

1. $6 \times \square = 3 \times 5 \times 2$
2. $7 \times 5 \div 7 + 24 + \square = 60$
3. $5 \times \square = 49 \div 7 + 3$
4. $23 + \square + 14 = 27 + 22$
5. $56 \div 7 = 2 + 46 \div \square$
6. $\square = 4 \times 6 \div 8 \times 9 - 5$
7. $73 - \square = 18 - 7 \times 6$
8. $57 - 5 = 10 \times 6 - \square$
9. $24 - \square - 7 = 48 \div 6$
10. $\square = 7 \times 8 - 6 \times 3 - 100$

Ex 25	Ex 26
1 **14**	**8**
2 **58**	**9**
3 **4**	**1**
4 **3**	**11**
5 **8**	**9**
6 **8**	**14**
7 **7**	**44**
8 **26**	**51**
9 **69**	**9**
10 **13**	**7**

Exercise C25

1. $34 + 44 = 52 + 12 + \square$
2. $71 - 13 - 10 + 21 - 11 = \square$
3. $6 \times 2 \times \square = 6 \times 8$
4. $\square \times 4 = 12 \times 3 \div 3$
5. $\square = 13 + 21 + 32 + 6 \div 9$
6. $24 + 26 \div 5 = 80 \div \square$
7. $50 = 9 \times 9 - 11 - 13 - \square$
8. $\square = 27 - 13 \times 2 - 15 \times 2$
9. $\square = 23 + 46 + 5 - 12 + 7$
10. $83 - \square = 51 + 7 + 12$

Exercise C26

1. $\square = 10 \times 7 \div 10 \times 8 \div 7$
2. $36 = 4 \times 2 \times 5 \div 10 \times \square$
3. $88 \div 8 + 43 + 24 + \square = 79$
4. $32 + 43 = 51 + \square + 13$
5. $4 \times \square = 6 \times 7 - 6$
6. $8 \times 9 = 90 - 4 - \square$
7. $21 + 26 + 21 = 24 + \square$
8. $\square = 63 + 9 - 14 + 6 - 13$
9. $\square = 108 \div 9 \div 4 \times 9 \div 3$
10. $84 \div 7 \div 3 \times 7 \div 4 = \square$

Ex 27	Ex 28
1 **68**	**4**
2 **21**	**13**
3 **120**	**13**
4 **11**	**44**
5 **12**	**7**
6 **58**	**8**
7 **6**	**63**
8 **108**	**7**
9 **3**	**6**
10 **9**	**100**

Exercise C27

1. $72 = 77 \div 7 + 21 \div 8 + \square$
2. $46 + \square = 42 + 12 + 13$
3. $32 - 11 - 13 \times 5 \times 3 = \square$
4. $66 - 13 = 8 \times 8 - \square$
5. $74 - \square = 87 - 15 - 10$
6. $90 - 12 - 15 + 9 - 14 = \square$
7. $8 \times 9 \div 8 \div 3 \times \square = 18$
8. $99 \div 11 \times 4 \div 3 \times 9 = \square$
9. $\square = 31 + 17 + 6 \div 6 \div 3$
10. $5 = 31 + 33 \div 8 + 37 \div \square$

Exercise C28

1. $87 - 14 - 12 - 11 \times \square = 200$
2. $24 - 13 \times 8 - 12 - \square = 63$
3. $79 = 84 - 14 - 11 + 7 + \square$
4. $\square = 71 - 15 + 13 - 14 - 11$
5. $36 \div 4 = 9 \times 7 \div \square$
6. $56 \div 7 \times 4 = \square \times 4$
7. $15 + 13 + 12 \div 10 + \square = 67$
8. $49 \div \square = 36 \div 9 + 3$
9. $83 - 11 = 6 \times 2 \times \square$
10. $\square = 4 \times 4 \times 2 - 12 \times 5$

ONE-A-WEEK – Mental Arithmetic Tests Book 3 © Folens

Exercise C29

1. $55 + \square = 32 + 24 + 13$
2. $9 \times 8 + 6 = 84 - \square$
3. $\square = 73 - 11 + 15 - 13 + 9$
4. $7 + 61 - 8 - 15 - 12 = \square$
5. $9 \times 7 = 88 - 13 - \square$
6. $26 + 51 = 21 + 34 + \square$
7. $62 = 22 + 23 \div 5 \div 3 + \square$
8. $23 + 51 - 11 \div 7 \div \square = 3$
9. $51 = 88 - 13 + 5 - 15 - \square$
10. $41 + 15 + 32 - 14 - \square = 63$

Exercise C30

1. $9 \times 2 \times 2 = \square + 12$
2. $\square \times 19 = 12 \times 3 + 2$
3. $79 = 81 \div 9 \times 7 + 13 + \square$
4. $42 \div 6 = 7 \times 9 \div \square$
5. $\square = 8 \times 3 + 11 \div 7 \times 8$
6. $\square = 96 \div 8 - 3 \times 7 - 14$
7. $78 - 11 = 87 - 15 - \square$
8. $82 - 13 - 13 = \square \times 8$
9. $11 \times 8 - 8 \div 10 \times \square = 32$
10. $\square = 16 \div 8 \times 16 \div 4 \times 5$

Exercise C31

1. $22 + 20 = 2 \times 3 \times \square$
2. $90 - 5 - 14 + 5 - 12 = \square$
3. $10 \times 9 - 12 - 14 + 15 = \square$
4. $\square = 29 - 11 \times 2 - 15 + 55$
5. $55 = 2 \times 19 + 41 - 10 - \square$
6. $72 - 12 + 19 - 10 - 13 = \square$
7. $77 - \square = 14 + 21 + 30$
8. $28 \div 4 = 100 \div 10 - \square$
9. $48 - 14 + \square = 61 - 11$
10. $\square = 90 \div 10 + 72 - 11 \div 10$

Exercise C32

1. $5 \times 5 + 52 \div 7 \times 9 = \square$
2. $\square = 6 \times 9 \div 6 + 12 \div 7$
3. $34 + 14 \div 6 \times 4 \div \square = 4$
4. $40 \div \square = 23 + 22 \div 9$
5. $5 \times 7 \div 5 \times 3 + 58 = \square$
6. $35 \div 7 \times 9 \div 5 \times \square = 27$
7. $\square = 12 \times 7 - 14 \div 7 \div 10$
8. $2 \times 6 = 24 \div 6 \times \square$
9. $5 \times 6 \div 3 \div 5 \times 16 = \square$
10. $21 \div 7 \times \square = 39 - 12$

Exercise C33

1. $36 + 22 + 6 - 8 - \square = 51$
2. $49 = 32 + 8 + 6 + 8 - \square$
3. $5 \times 2 \times 7 \div 10 \times \square = 35$
4. $\square = 72 \div 9 \div 4 \times 9 \div 6$
5. $83 - 11 = 6 \times 2 \times \square$
6. $\square = 96 \div 8 + 33 + 5 \div 10$
7. $57 - 9 - 8 - 10 \times \square = 90$
8. $\square = 11 + 12 + 5 \div 4 + 14$
9. $21 + 26 + 21 = 24 + \square$
10. $2 + 28 + 6 - 8 + \square = 30$

Exercise C34

1. $48 \div 6 \times \square = 10 \times 4$
2. $3 \times \square = 81 \div 9 \div 3$
3. $36 \div \square = 24 \div 6 + 5$
4. $\square = 31 + 17 + 6 \div 6 \div 3$
5. $38 - 6 = 4 \times 2 \times \square$
6. $42 = 26 - 6 \times 3 - 10 - \square$
7. $71 - 13 - 10 + 21 - 11 = \square$
8. $\square = 33 + 26 - 6 + 8 - 7$
9. $\square = 2 \times 6 \times 6 \div 6 \times 5$
10. $36 \div 4 = 9 \times 7 \div \square$

	Ex 29	Ex 30
1	14	24
2	6	2
3	73	3
4	33	9
5	12	40
6	22	49
7	59	5
8	3	7
9	14	4
10	11	40

	Ex 31	Ex 32
1	7	99
2	64	3
3	79	8
4	76	8
5	14	79
6	56	3
7	12	1
8	3	3
9	16	32
10	7	9

	Ex 33	Ex 34
1	5	5
2	5	1
3	5	4
4	3	3
5	6	4
6	5	8
7	3	58
8	21	54
9	44	60
10	2	7

Ex 35	Ex 36
1 26	21
2 63	37
3 31	29
4 26	9
5 36	6
6 13	9
7 28	3
8 3	8
9 9	4
10 59	120

Exercise C35

1. $25 + 14 = 4 + 9 + \square$
2. $15 + 13 + 12 \div 10 + \square = 67$
3. $59 - 8 - 4 - 7 - 9 = \square$
4. $\square = 27 - 13 \times 2 - 15 \times 2$
5. $50 - 2 - 9 + 7 - 10 = \square$
6. $79 = 84 - 14 - 11 + 7 + \square$
7. $\square = 30 \div 5 \times 7 \div 6 \times 4$
8. $\square \times 4 = 12 \times 3 \div 3$
9. $25 = 48 \div 4 \div 4 + 13 + \square$
10. $84 \div 7 + 32 \div 4 + 48 = \square$

Exercise C36

1. $41 - 8 - 3 - 4 - 5 = \square$
2. $\square = 7 \times 8 - 5 - 8 - 6$
3. $\square = 39 - 6 - 6 + 7 - 5$
4. $62 - 9 = 13 + 31 + \square$
5. $10 \times 9 \div 10 \times 4 \div \square = 6$
6. $\square = 108 \div 9 \div 4 \times 9 \div 3$
7. $40 \div 5 = 25 \div 5 + \square$
8. $24 + 26 \div 5 = 80 \div \square$
9. $51 - 5 - \square = 6 \times 7$
10. $32 - 11 - 13 \times 5 \times 3 = \square$

Ex 37	Ex 38
1 4	4
2 16	40
3 12	38
4 8	8
5 7	2
6 46	6
7 21	1
8 39	9
9 11	14
10 9	32

Exercise C37

1. $33 = 2 \times 4 + 32 - 3 - \square$
2. $35 - 8 + 3 - 20 + \square = 26$
3. $9 \times 7 = 88 - 13 - \square$
4. $46 = 51 - 4 + 12 - 5 - \square$
5. $11 + 23 = \square \times 4 + 6$
6. $27 + 12 + 2 = \square - 5$
7. $12 \div 3 - 2 + 12 + 7 = \square$
8. $\square = 66 - 8 + 2 \div 6 + 29$
9. $41 + 15 + 32 - 14 - \square = 63$
10. $36 \div 6 + 37 + 3 - \square = 37$

Exercise C38

1. $40 \div 5 = 21 + 11 \div \square$
2. $\square = 8 \times 3 + 11 \div 7 \times 8$
3. $7 + 16 + 3 + 5 + 7 = \square$
4. $40 \div \square = 23 + 22 \div 9$
5. $45 \div 5 = 28 \div 4 + \square$
6. $36 = 36 \div 3 \times 5 \div 10 \times \square$
7. $42 \div 6 - \square = 24 \div 4$
8. $24 - \square - 7 = 48 \div 6$
9. $\square = 12 \times 10 \div 10 \div 6 \times 7$
10. $5 \times 6 \div 3 \div 5 \times 16 = \square$

Ex 39	Ex 40
1 6	31
2 41	28
3 8	5
4 11	12
5 76	2
6 23	10
7 37	5
8 16	6
9 28	10
10 59	40

Exercise C39

1. $9 \times 8 + 6 = 84 - \square$
2. $\square = 4 \times 8 + 8 - 5 + 6$
3. $\square \times 8 = 75 - 3 - 8$
4. $45 + 14 = 6 \times 8 + \square$
5. $\square = 29 - 11 \times 2 - 15 + 55$
6. $72 \div 8 + \square = 39 - 7$
7. $\square = 21 + 7 \div 4 + 17 + 13$
8. $48 - 14 + \square = 71 - 12 - 9$
9. $58 = 3 + 45 \div 8 + 24 + \square$
10. $62 = 22 + 23 \div 5 \div 3 + \square$

Exercise C40

1. $3 + 6 \times 5 \div 5 + \square = 40$
2. $10 \times 6 \div 5 \div 3 \times 7 = \square$
3. $35 = 31 + 24 + 8 \div 9 \times \square$
4. $23 + \square + 14 = 27 + 22$
5. $\square \times 19 = 12 \times 3 + 2$
6. $4 \times 9 - 8 \div 4 \times \square = 70$
7. $78 - 11 = 87 - 15 - \square$
8. $9 = 72 \div 6 - 3 \times 6 \div \square$
9. $50 - 10 - 10 \times 4 \div \square = 12$
10. $\square = 16 \div 8 \times 16 \div 4 \times 5$

Section D

Exercise D1

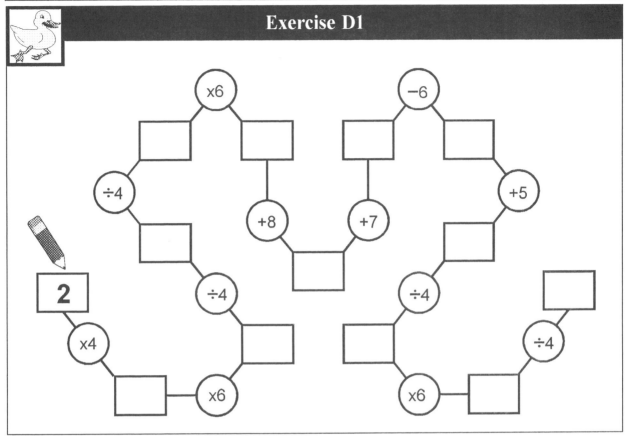

Exercise D2

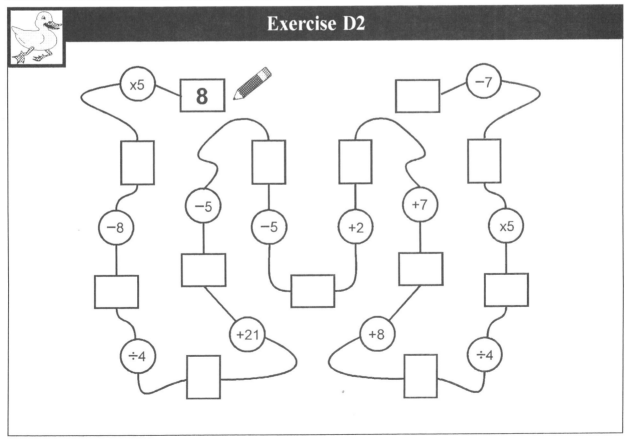

Exercise D3

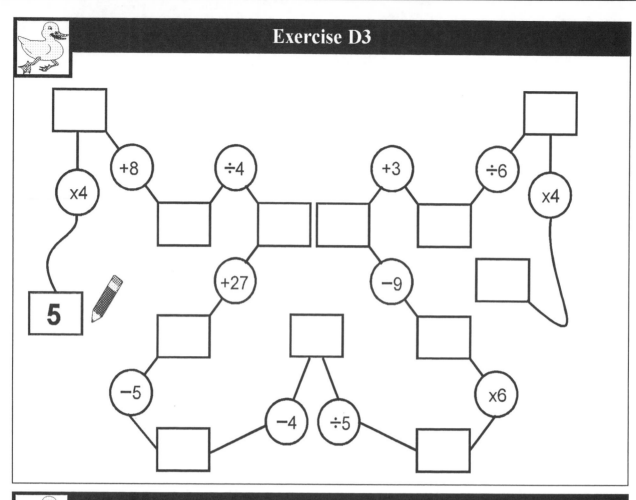

Exercise D4

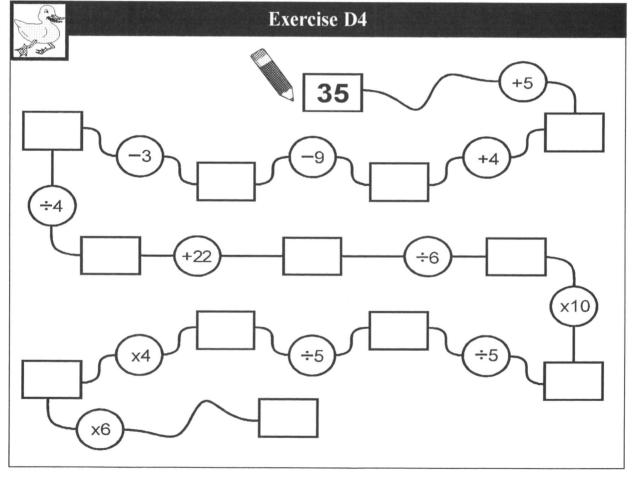

Exercise D5

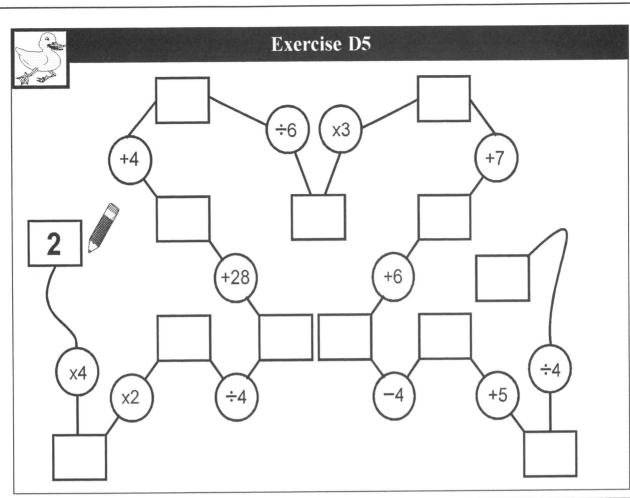

Exercise D6

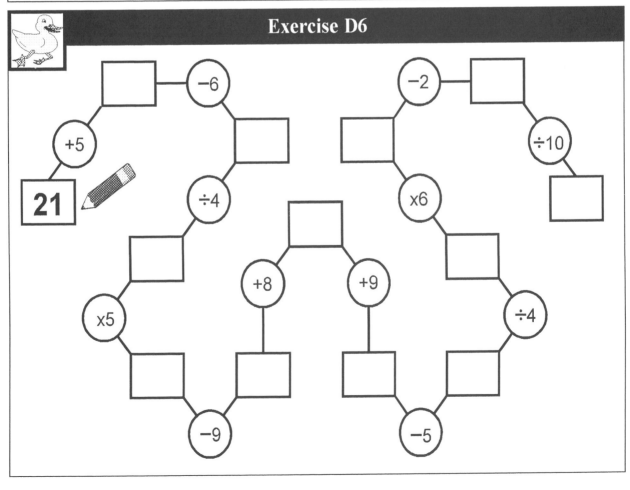

Exercise D7

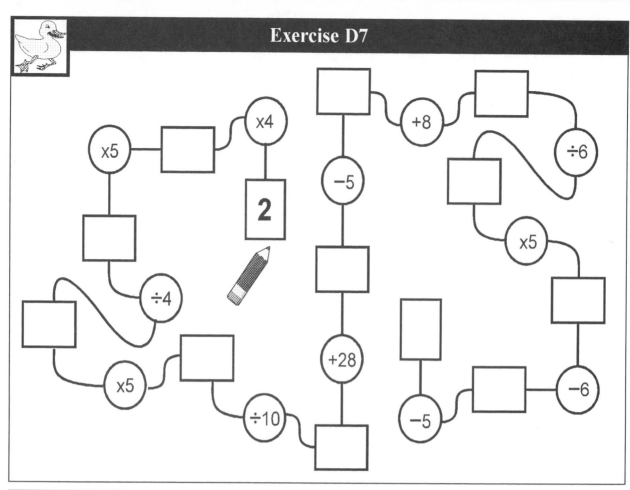

Exercise D8

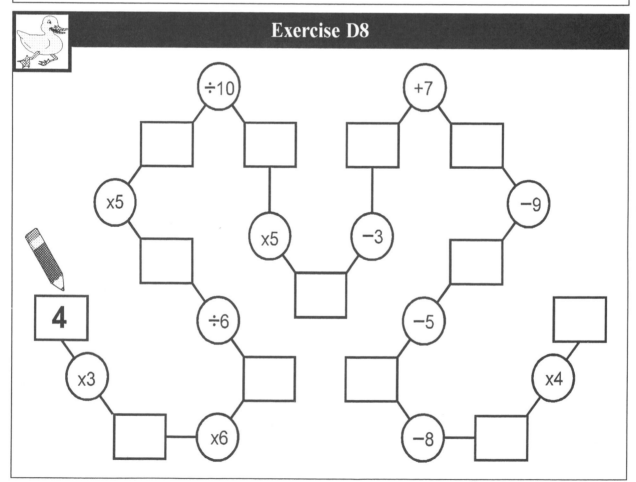

ONE-A-WEEK – *Mental Arithmetic Tests Book 3* © Folens (copiable page)

Exercise D9

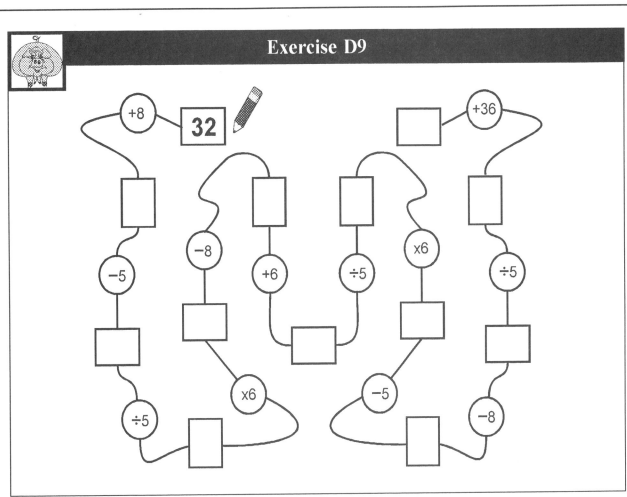

Exercise D10

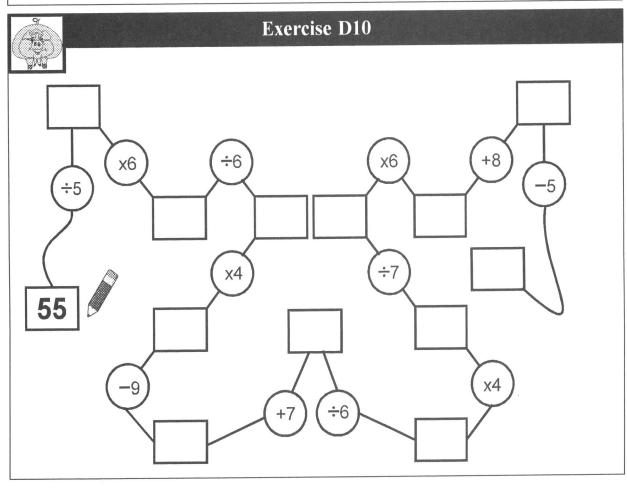

Exercise D11

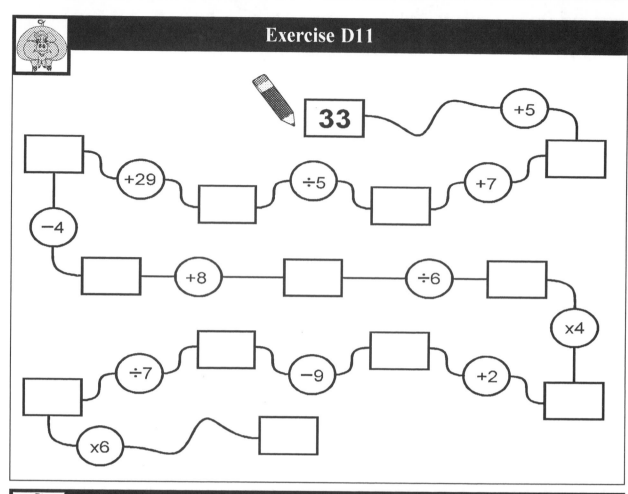

Exercise D12

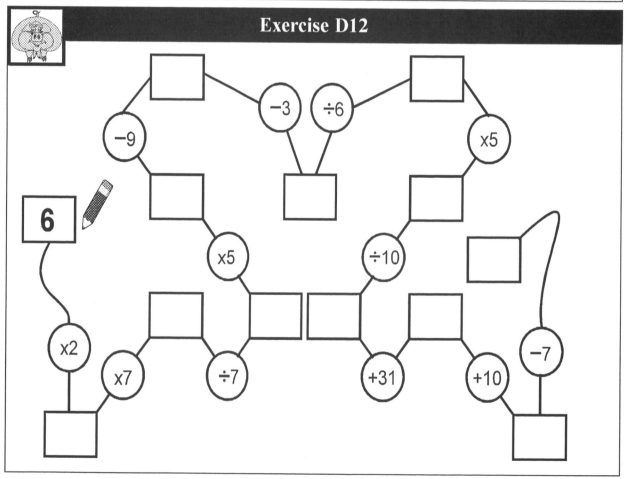

Exercise D13

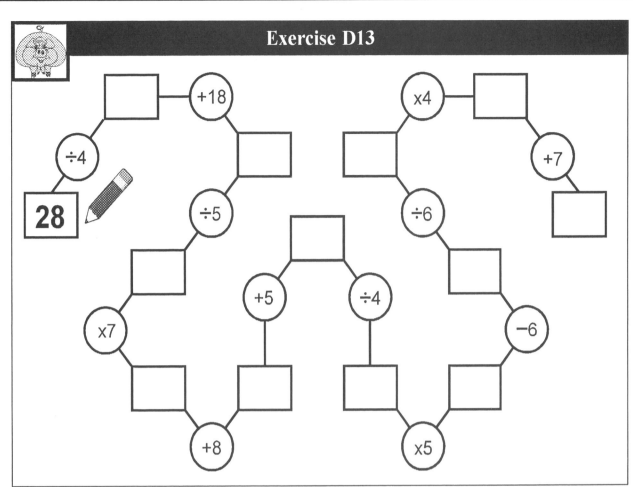

Exercise D14

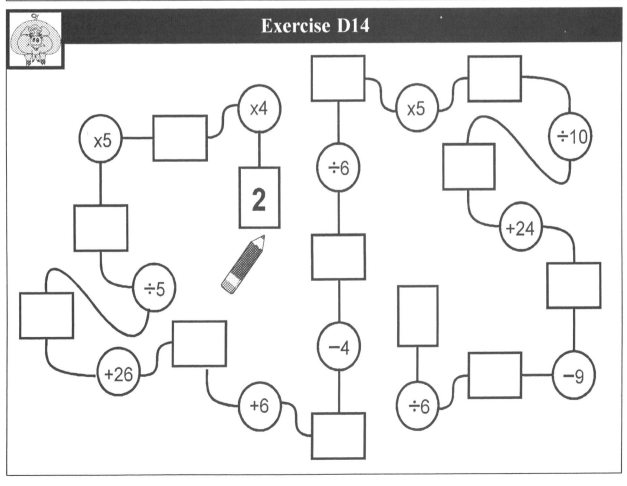

Exercise D15

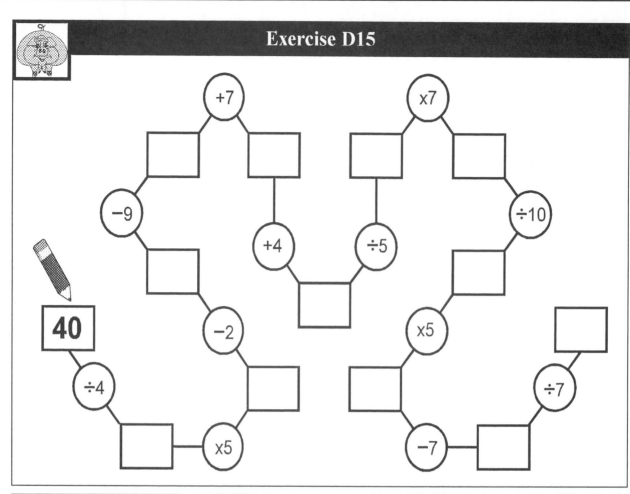

Exercise D16

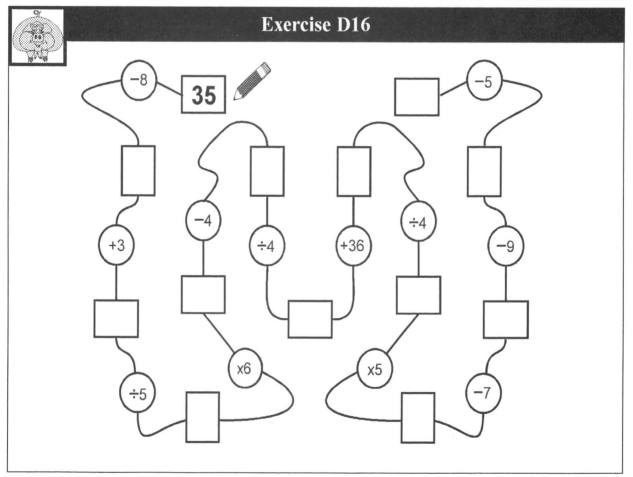

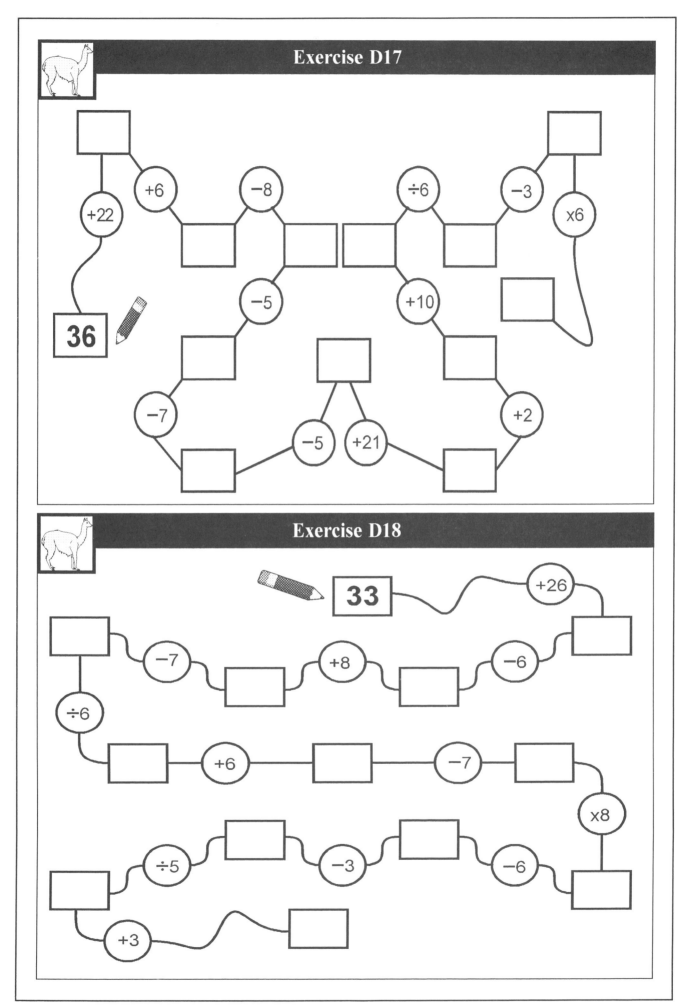

Exercise D17

Exercise D18

Exercise D19

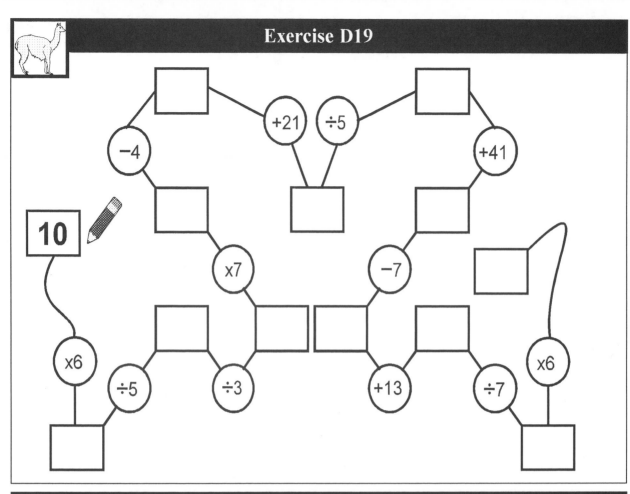

Exercise D20

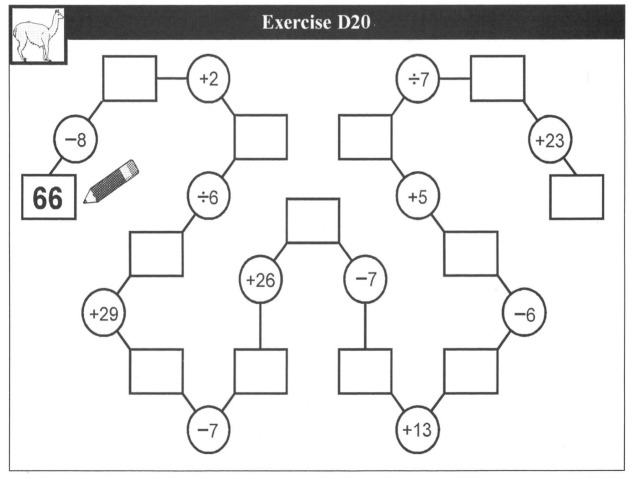

ONE-A-WEEK – *Mental Arithmetic Tests Book 3* © Folens (copiable page)

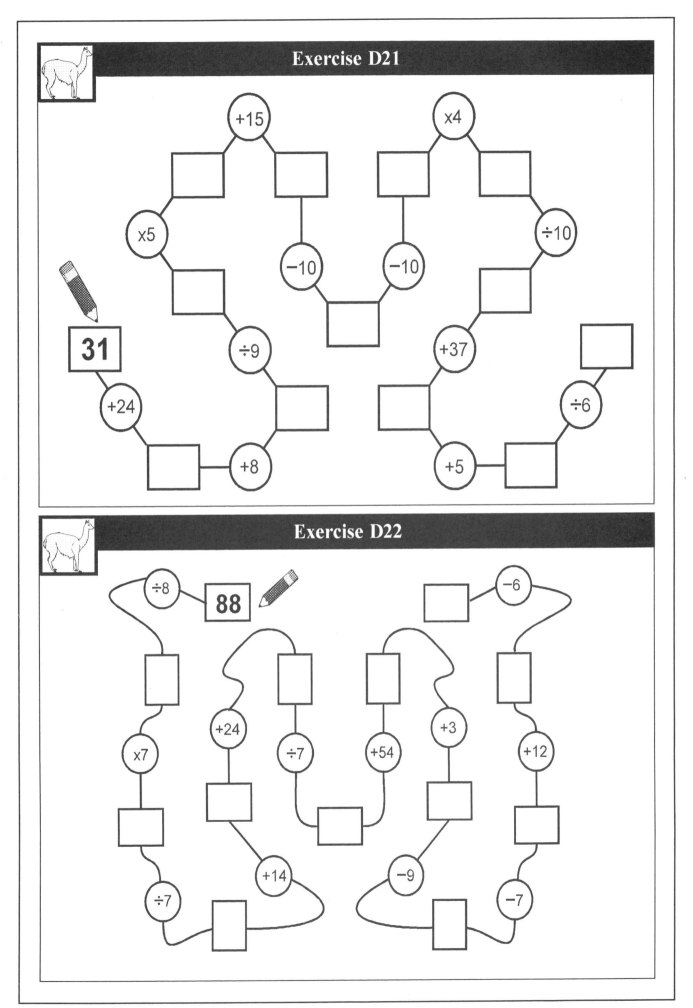

Exercise D21

Exercise D22

Exercise D23

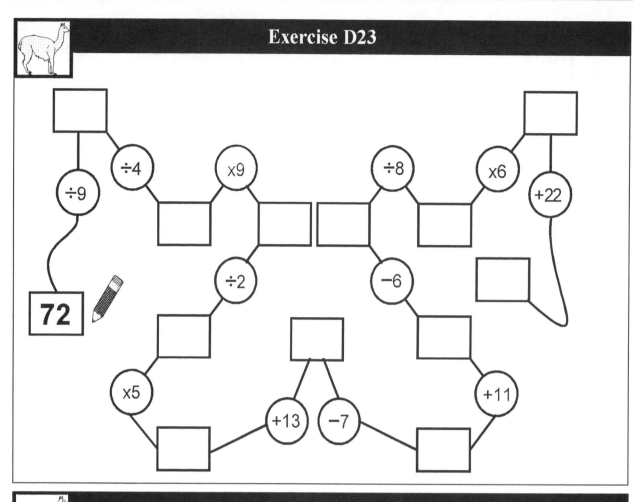

Exercise D24

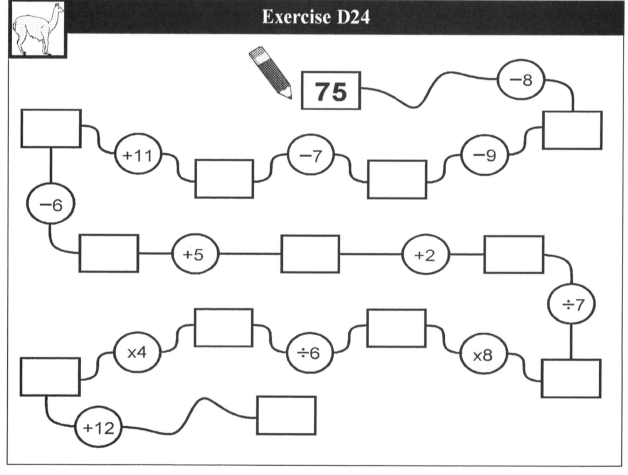

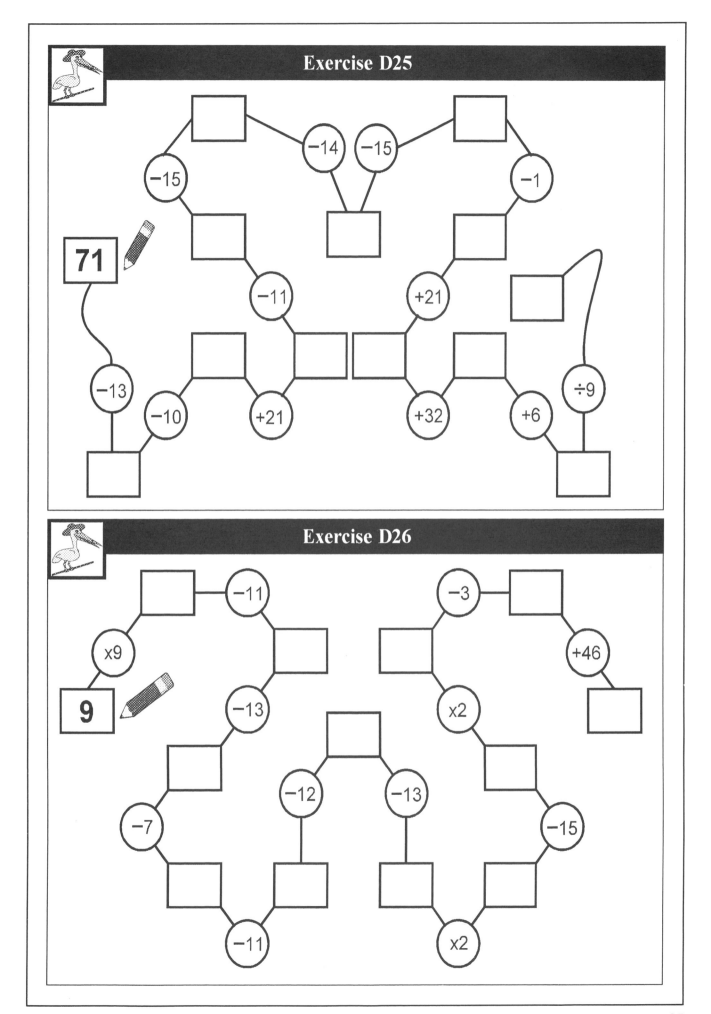

Exercise D25

71

Exercise D26

9

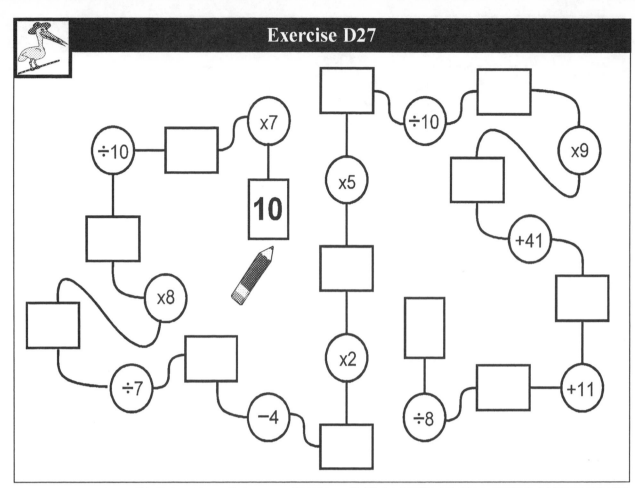

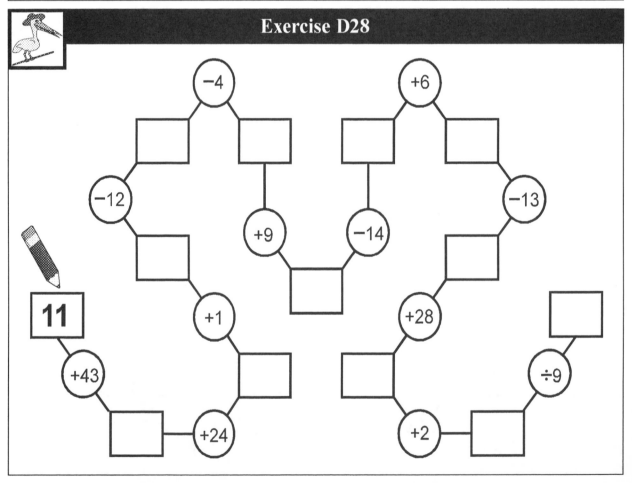

ONE-A-WEEK – *Mental Arithmetic Tests Book 3* © Folens (copiable page)

Exercise D29

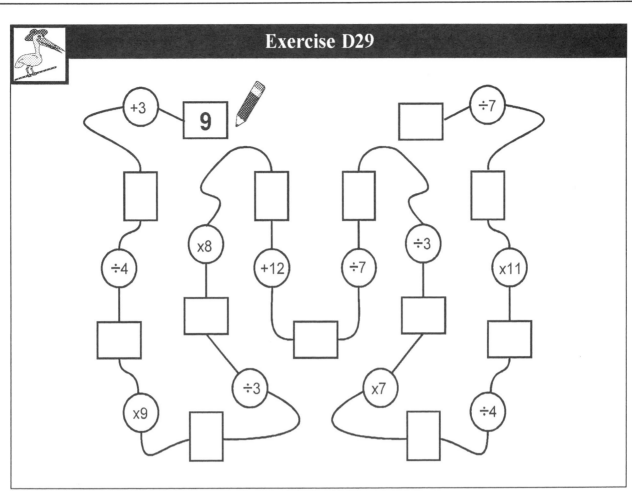

Exercise D30

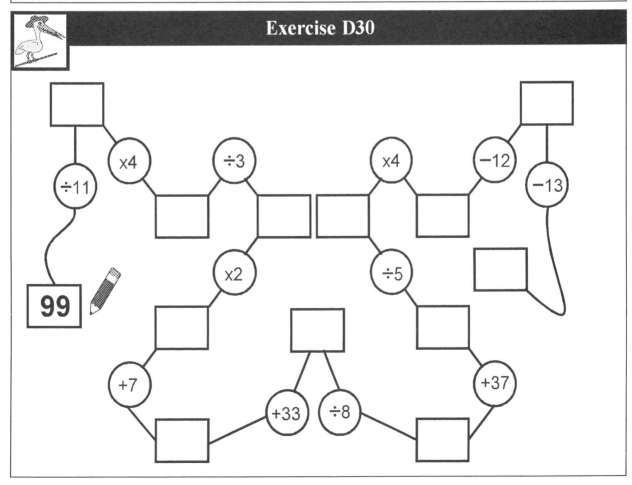

Exercise D31

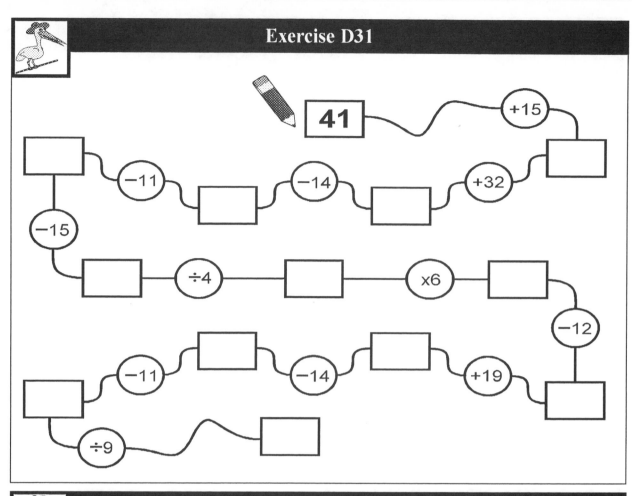

Exercise D32

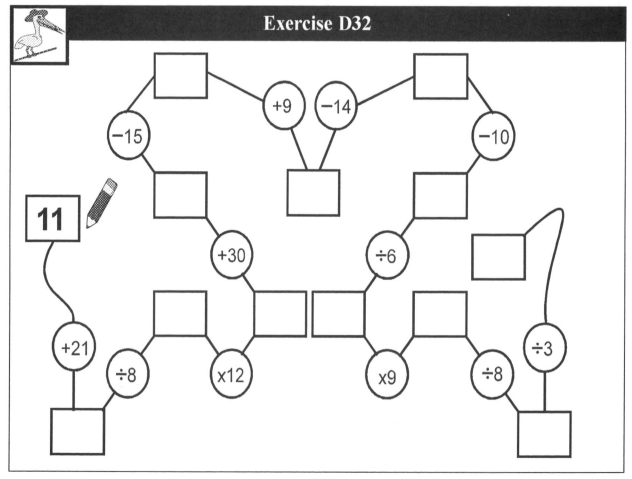

ONE-A-WEEK – *Mental Arithmetic Tests Book 3* © Folens (copiable page)

Exercise D33

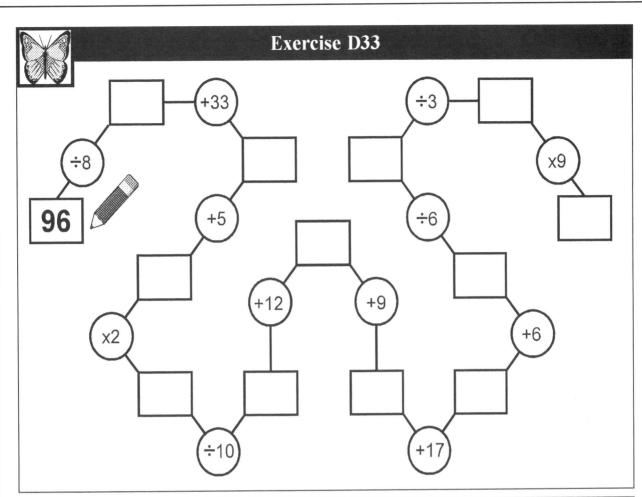

Exercise D34

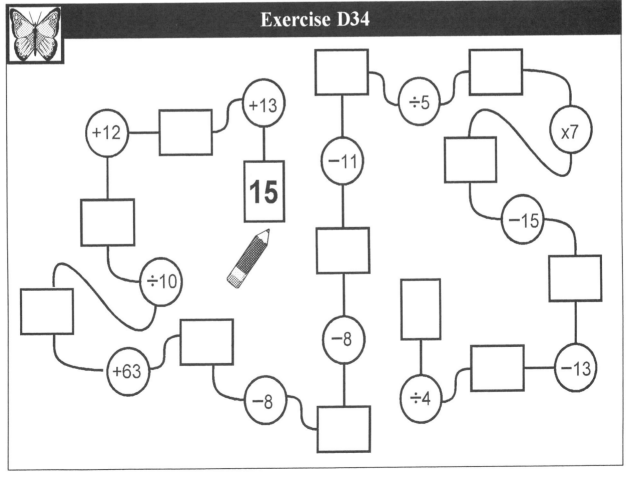

Exercise D35

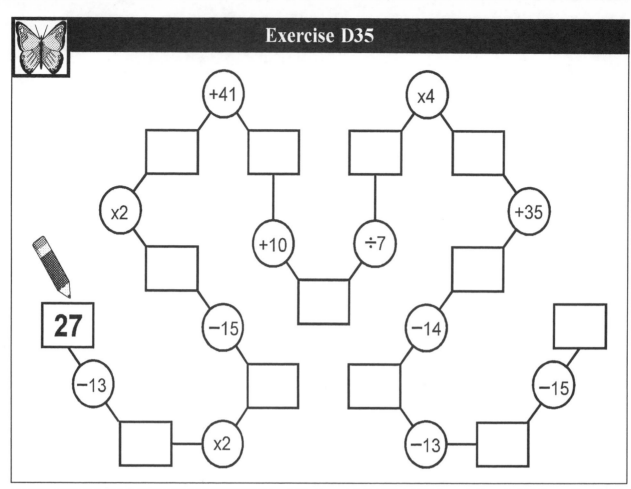

Exercise D36

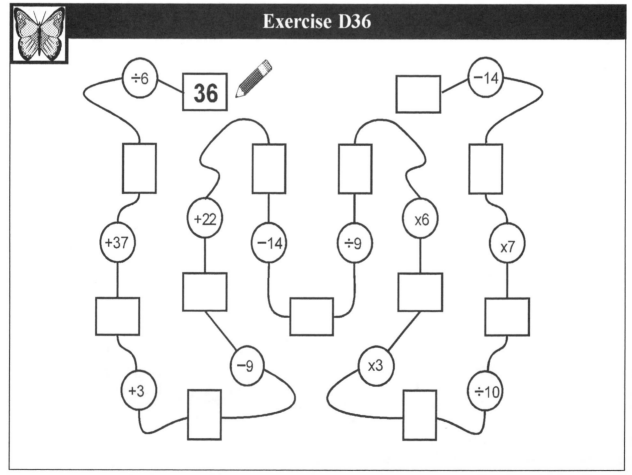

ONE-A-WEEK – *Mental Arithmetic Tests Book 3*

Exercise D37

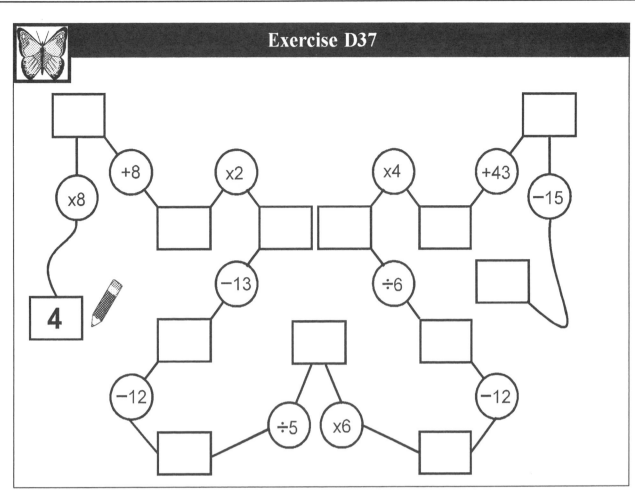

Exercise D38

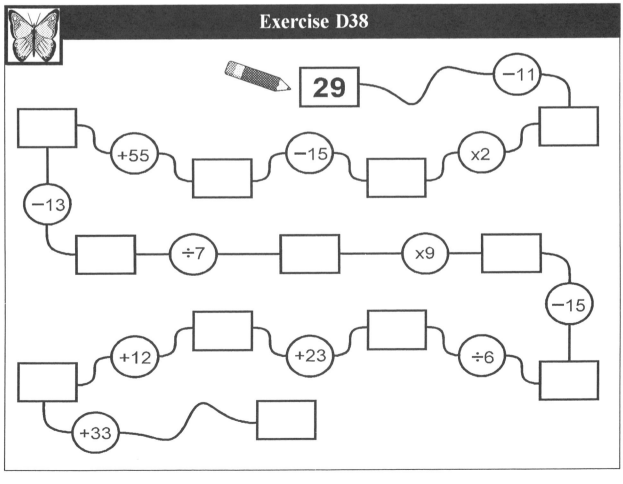

Exercise D39

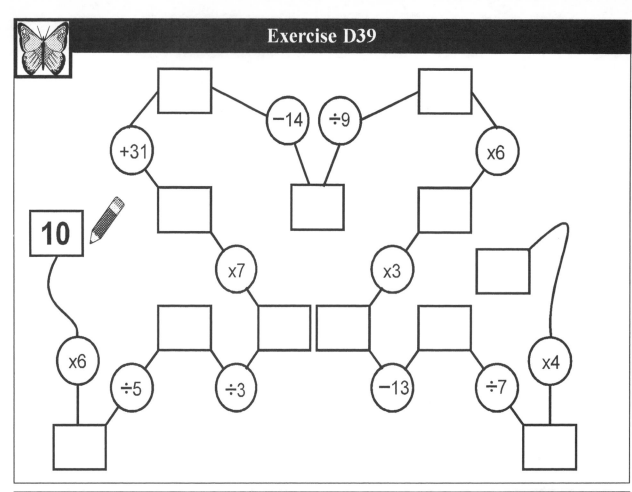

Exercise D40

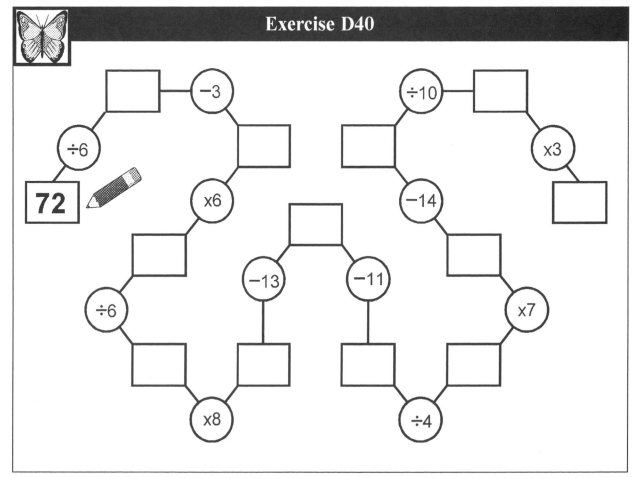

ONE-A-WEEK – *Mental Arithmetic Tests Book 3*

Section E

Exercise E1

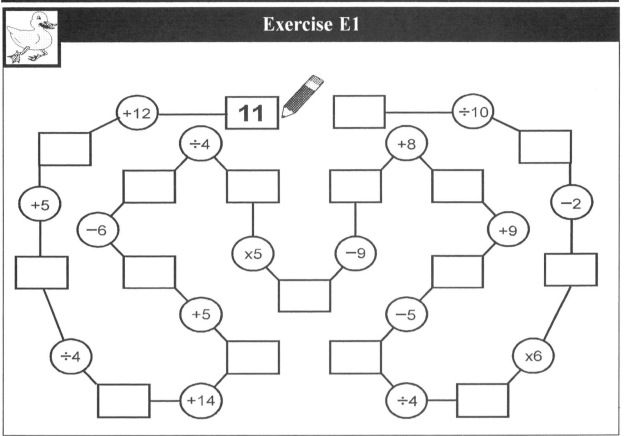

Exercise E2

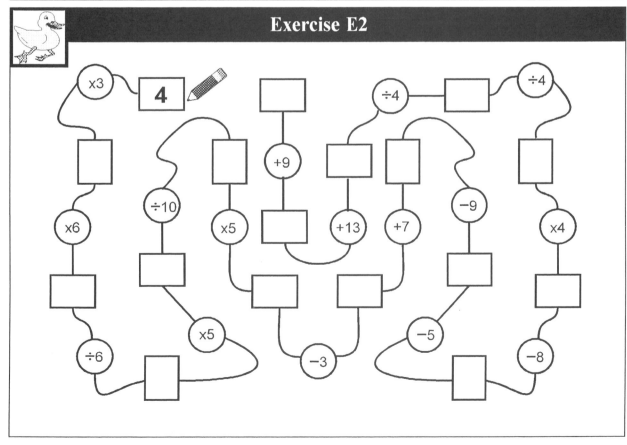

Exercise E3

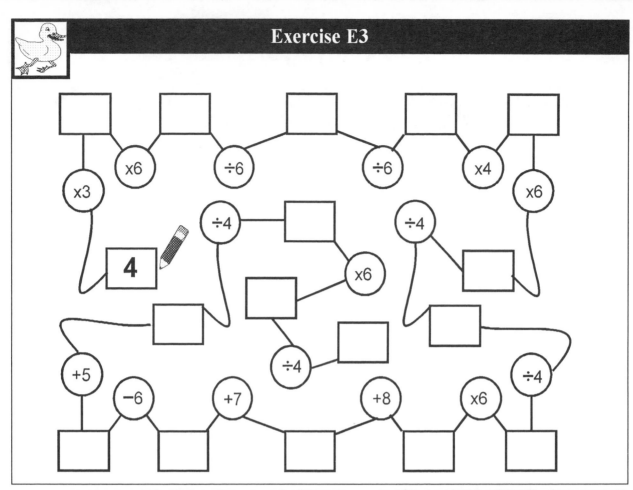

Exercise E4

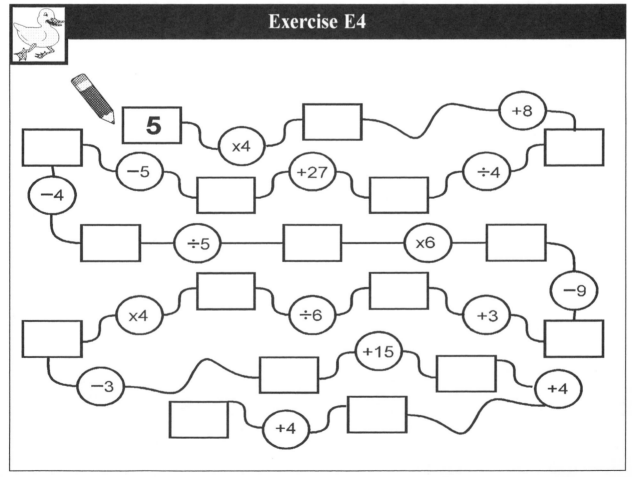

ONE-A-WEEK – *Mental Arithmetic Tests Book 3* © Folens (copiable page)

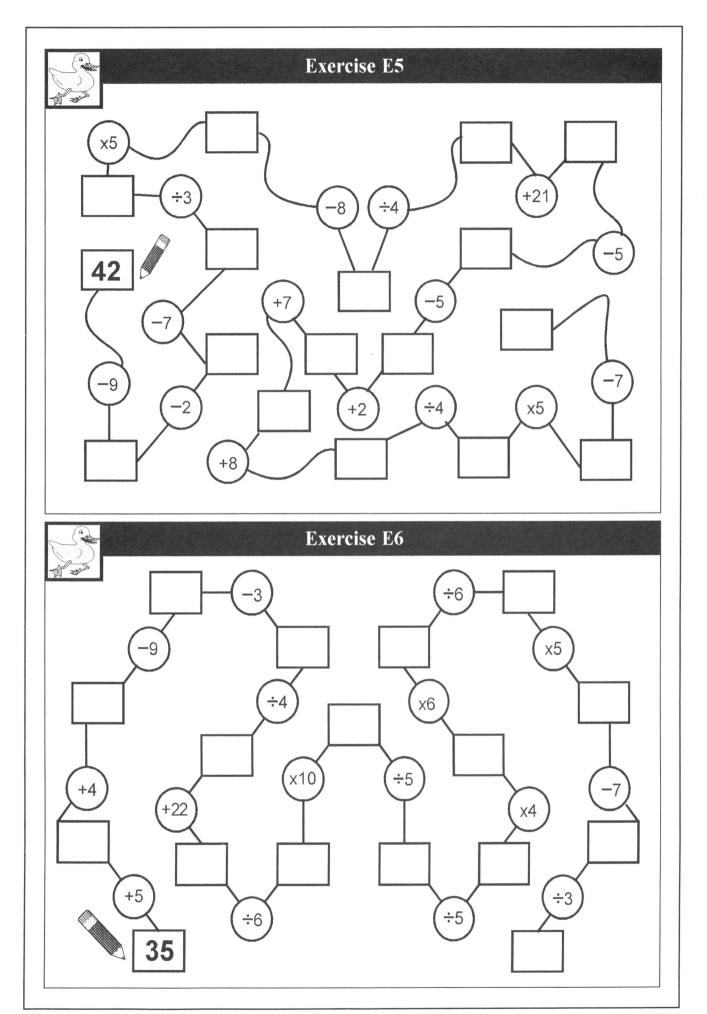

Exercise E5

Exercise E6

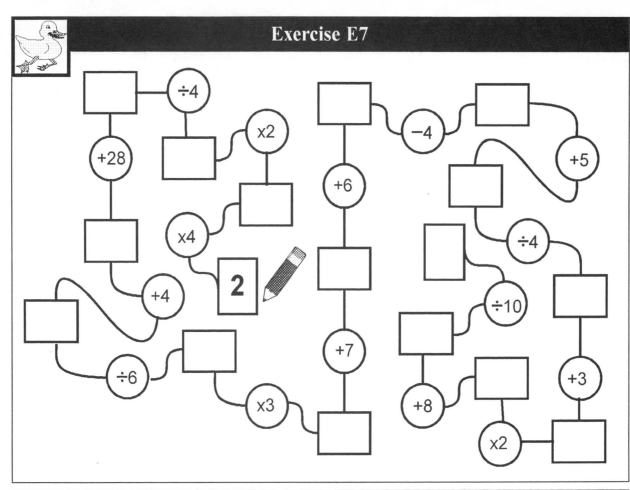

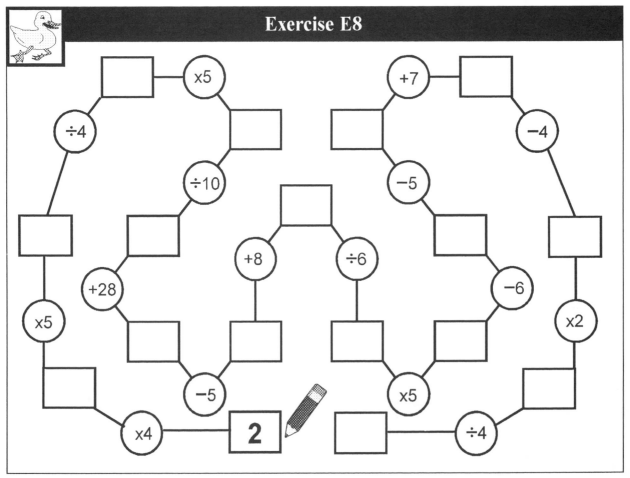

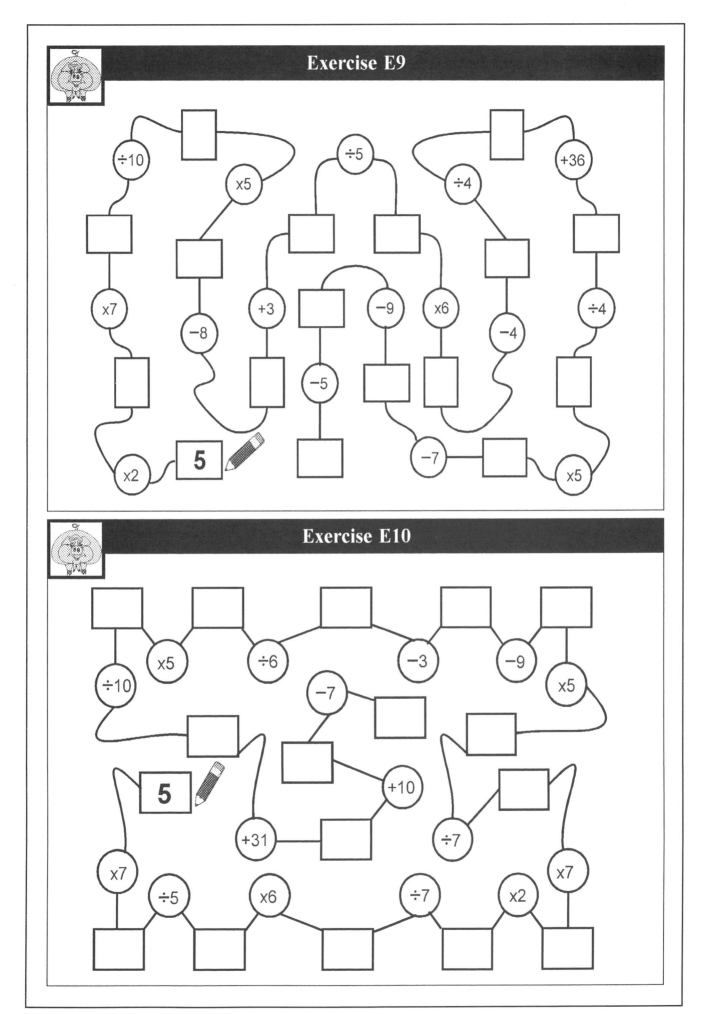

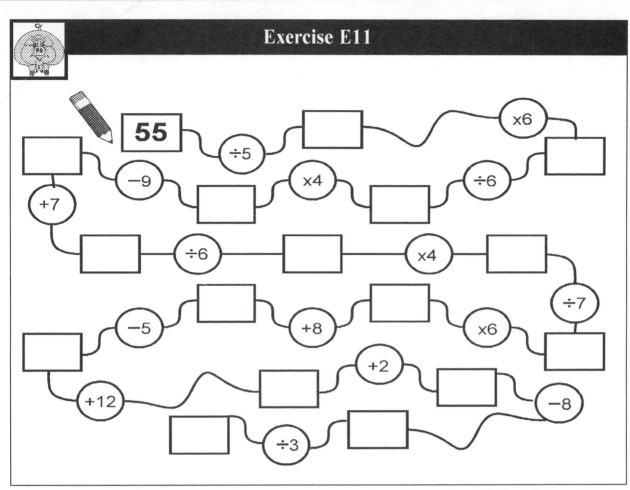

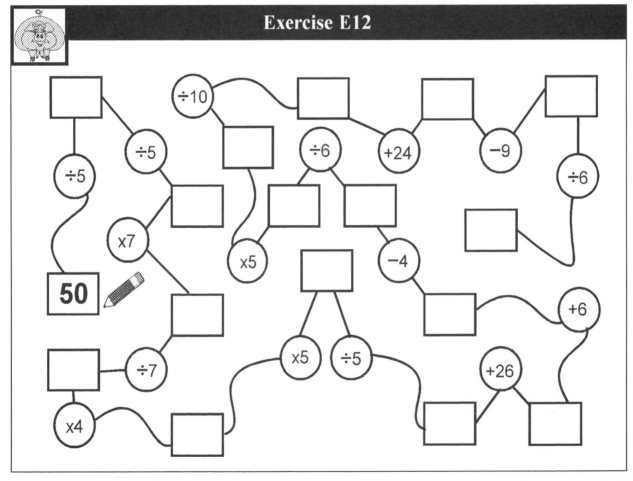

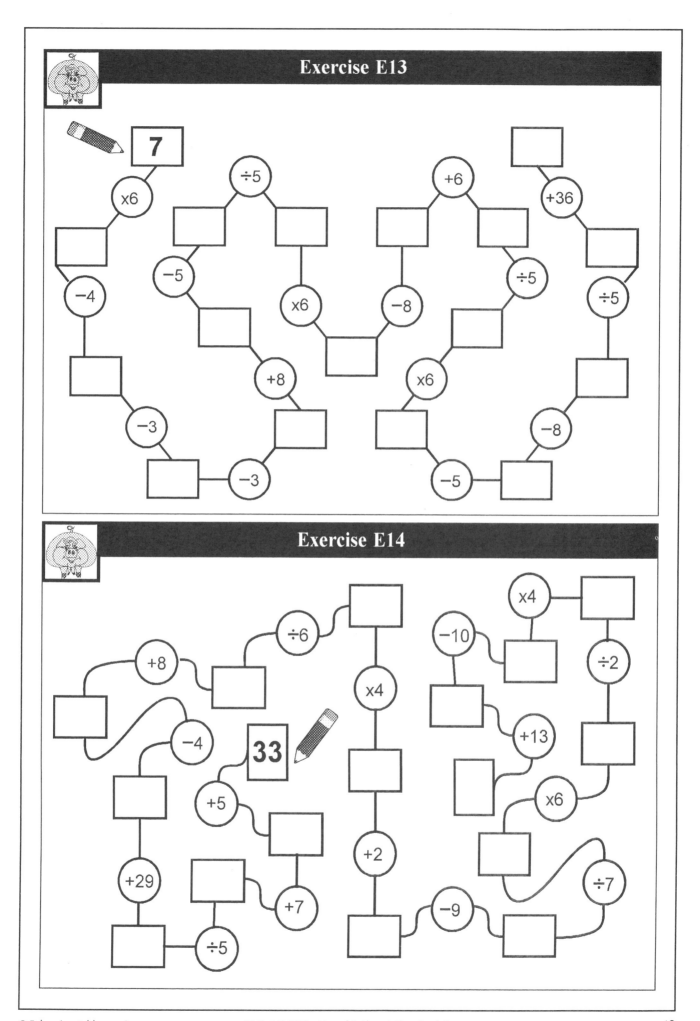

Exercise E13

Exercise E14

Exercise E15

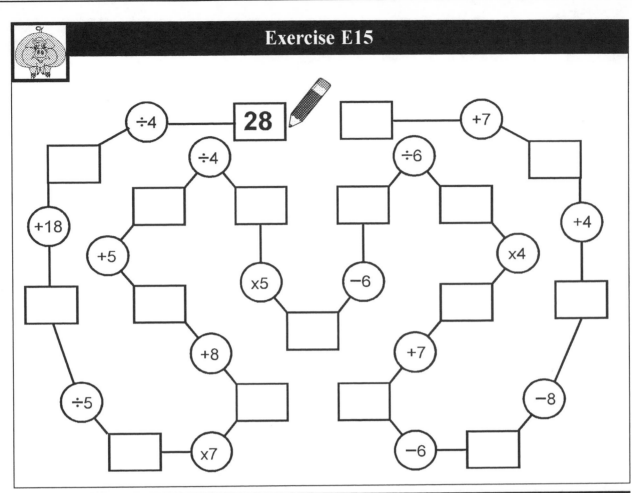

Exercise E16

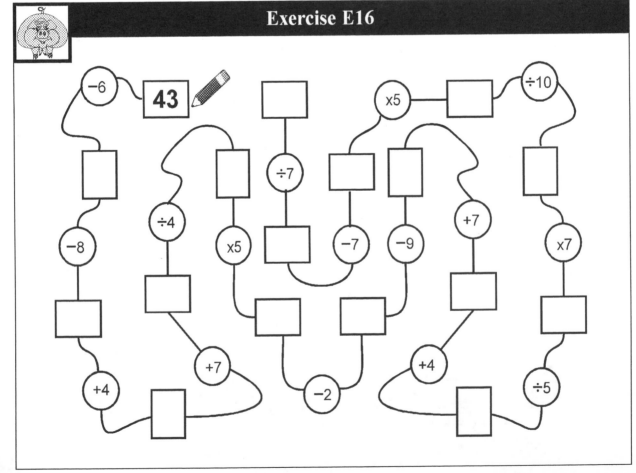

ONE-A-WEEK – *Mental Arithmetic Tests Book 3* © Folens (copiable page)

Exercise E17

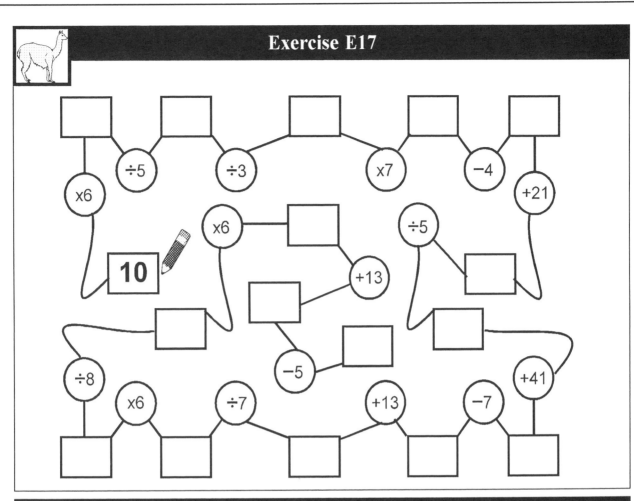

Exercise E18

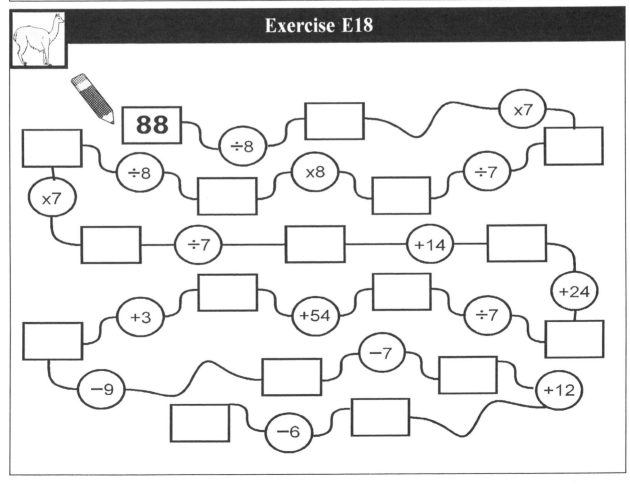

Exercise E19

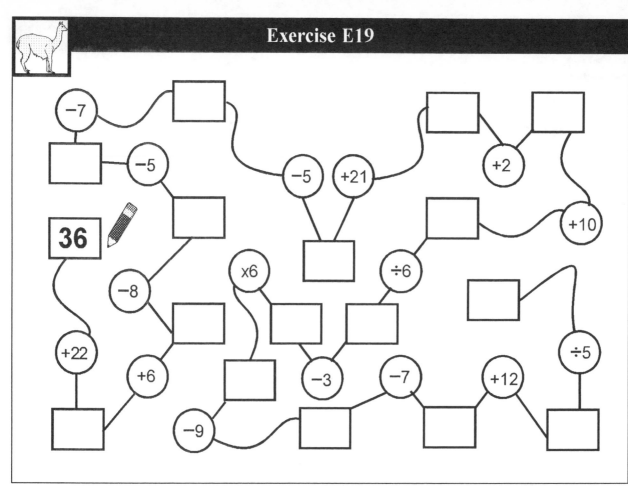

Exercise E20

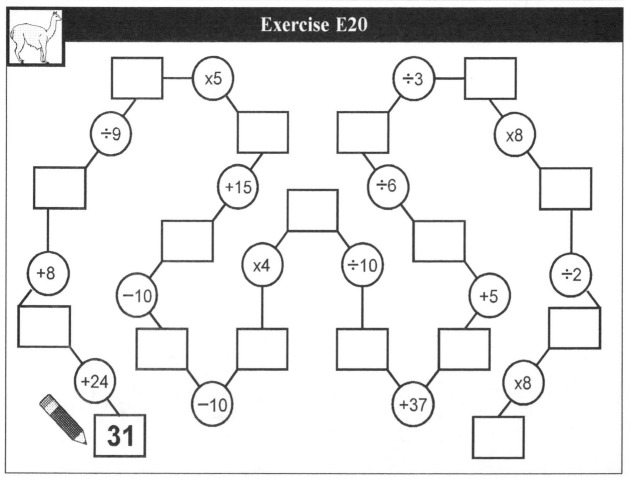

ONE-A-WEEK – *Mental Arithmetic Tests Book 3* © Folens (copiable page)

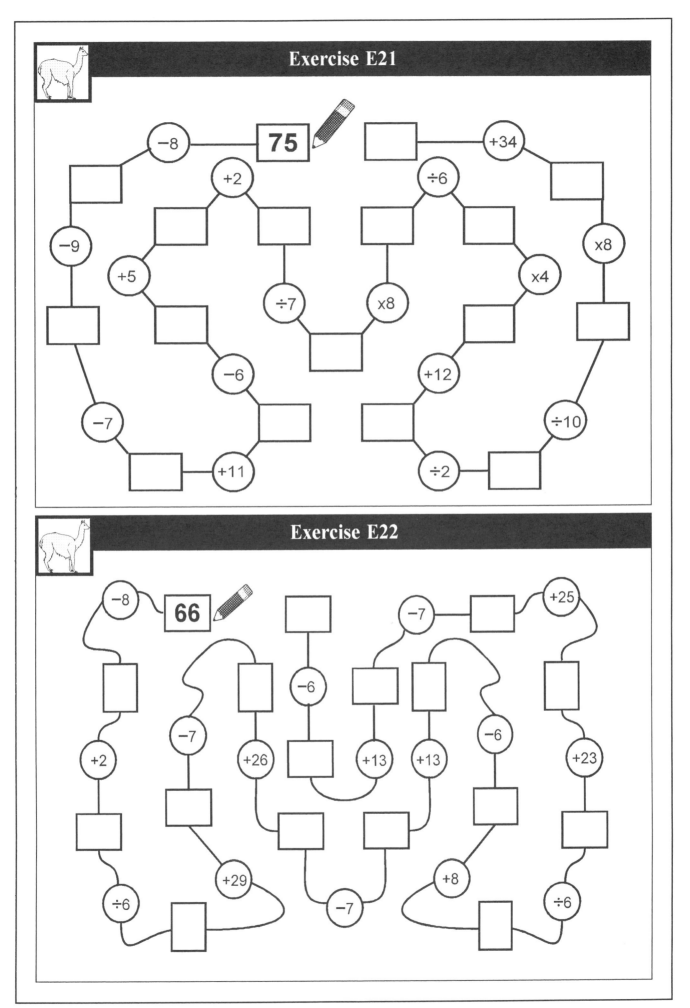

Exercise E21

75

Exercise E22

66

Exercise E23

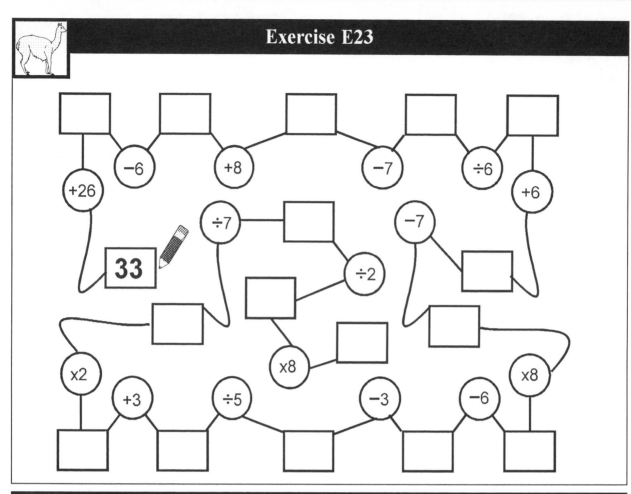

Exercise E24

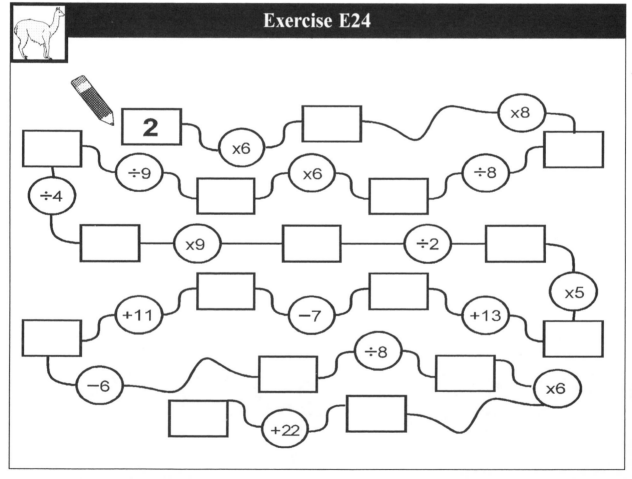

ONE-A-WEEK – *Mental Arithmetic Tests Book 3*
© Folens (copiable page)

Exercise E25

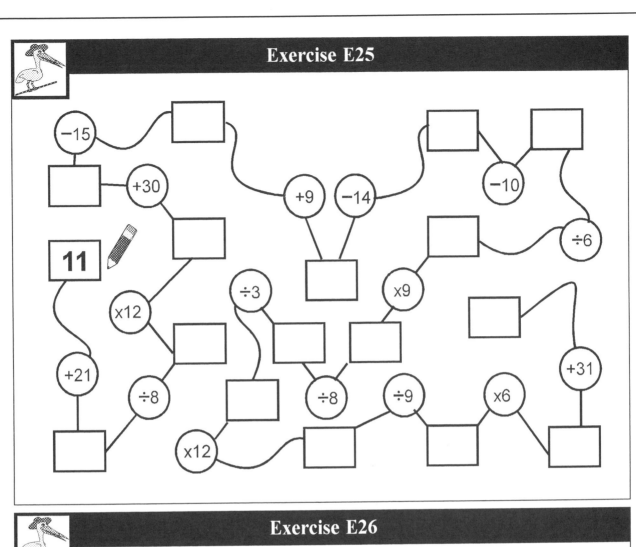

Exercise E26

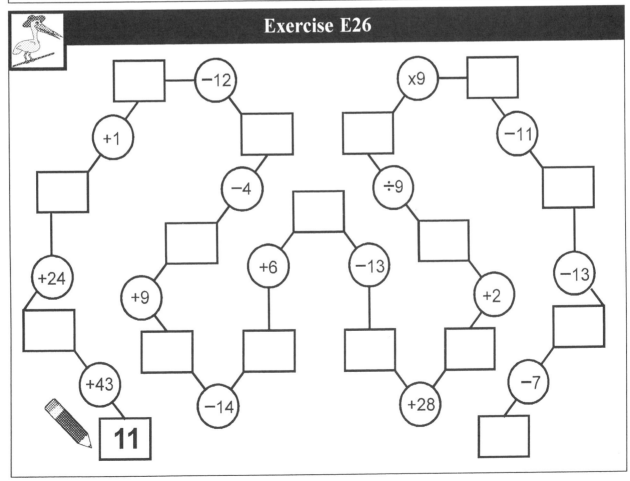

Exercise E27

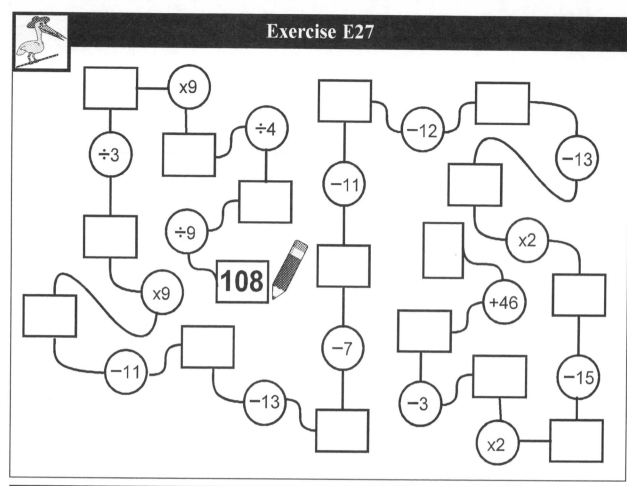

Exercise E28

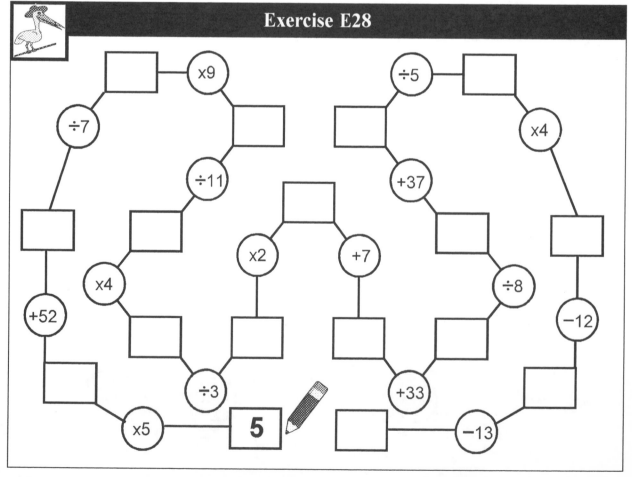

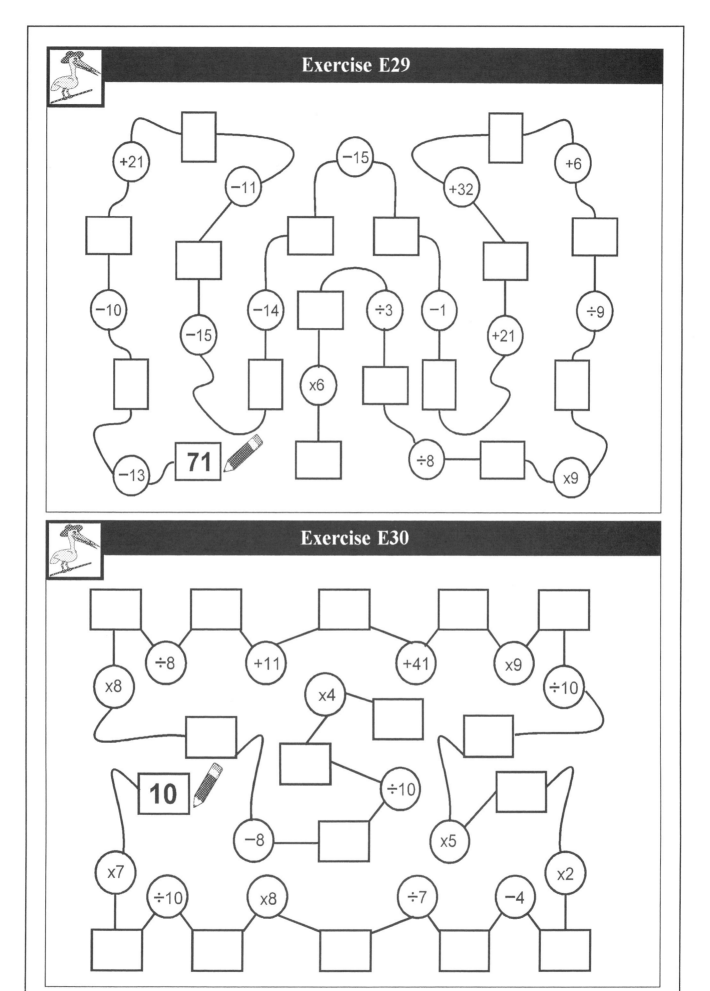

Exercise E29

Exercise E30

Exercise E31

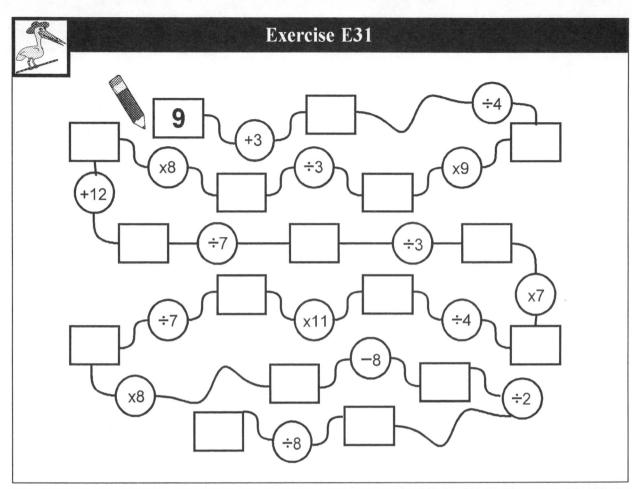

Exercise E32

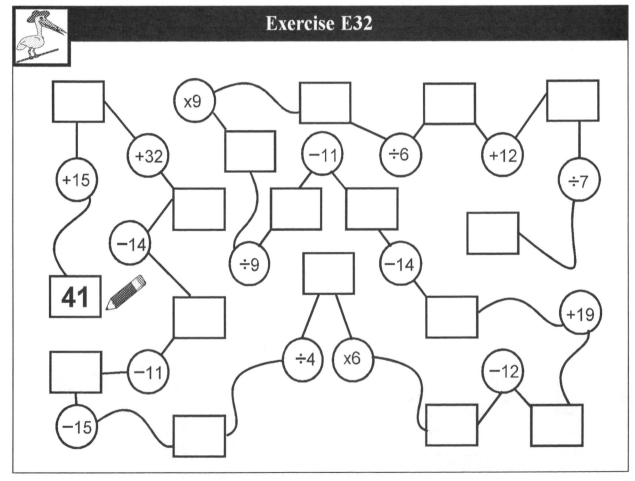

ONE-A-WEEK – *Mental Arithmetic Tests Book 3*   © Folens (copiable page)

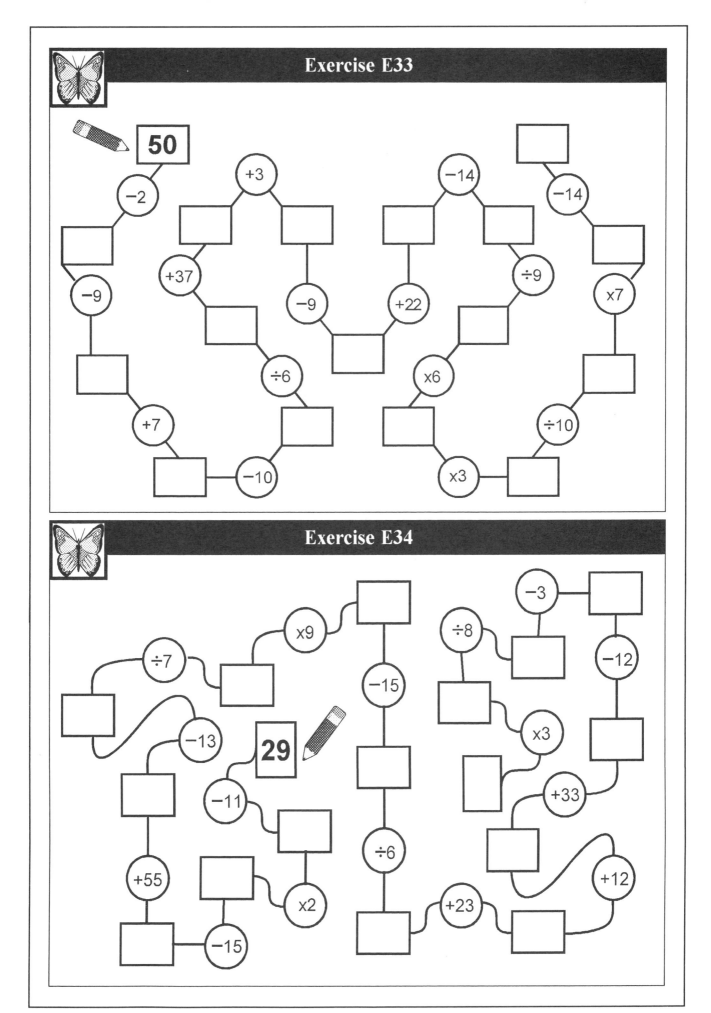

Exercise E33

Exercise E34

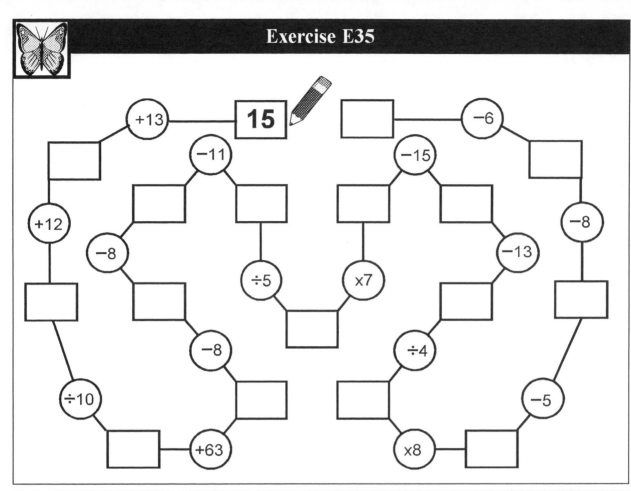

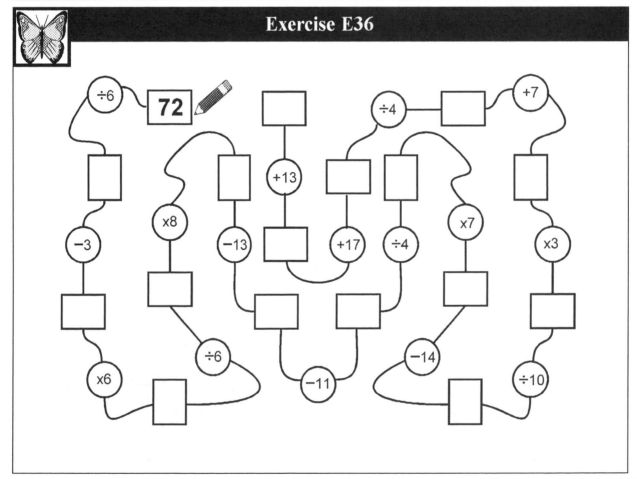

Exercise E37

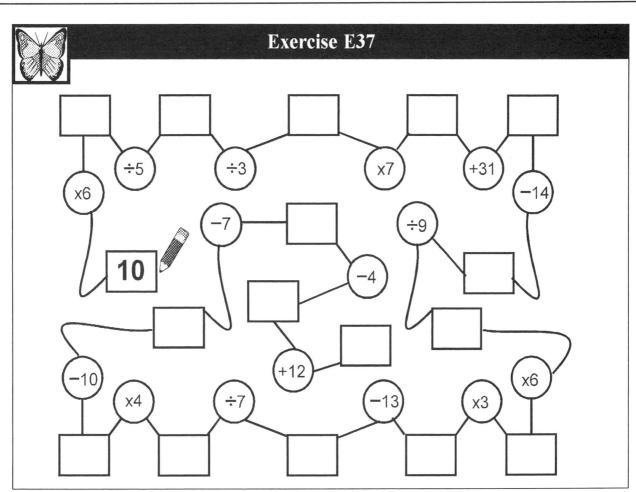

Exercise E38

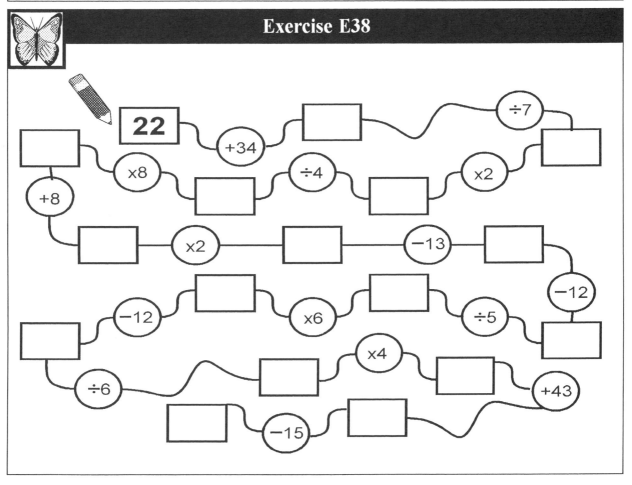

Exercise E39

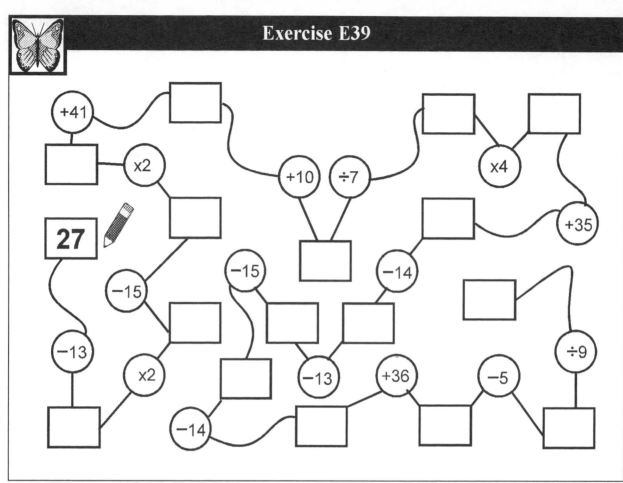

Exercise E40

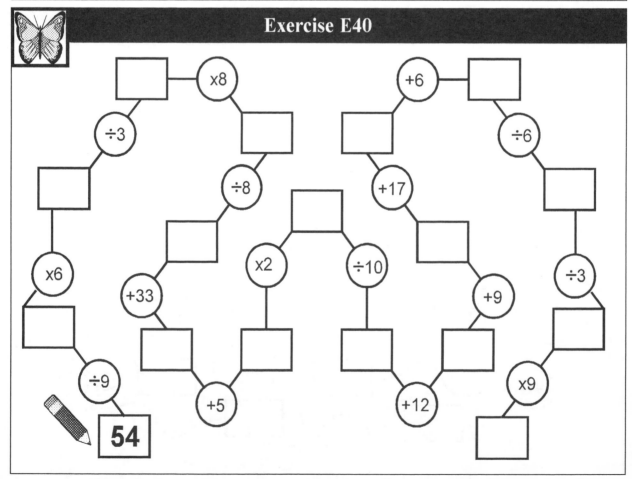

ONE-A-WEEK – *Mental Arithmetic Tests Book 3* © Folens (copiable page)

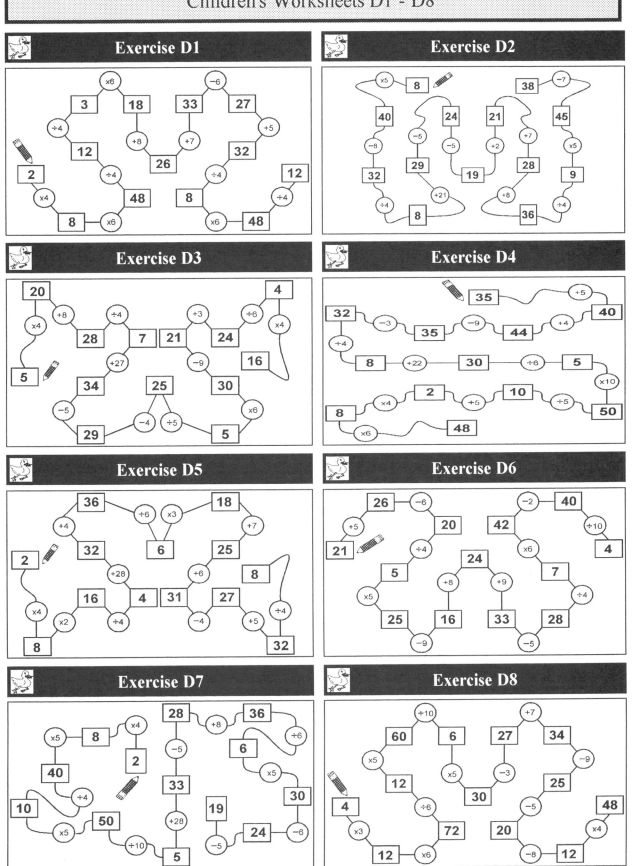

Answers to Section D

Children's Worksheets D1 - D8

Answers to Section D

Children's Worksheets D9 - D16

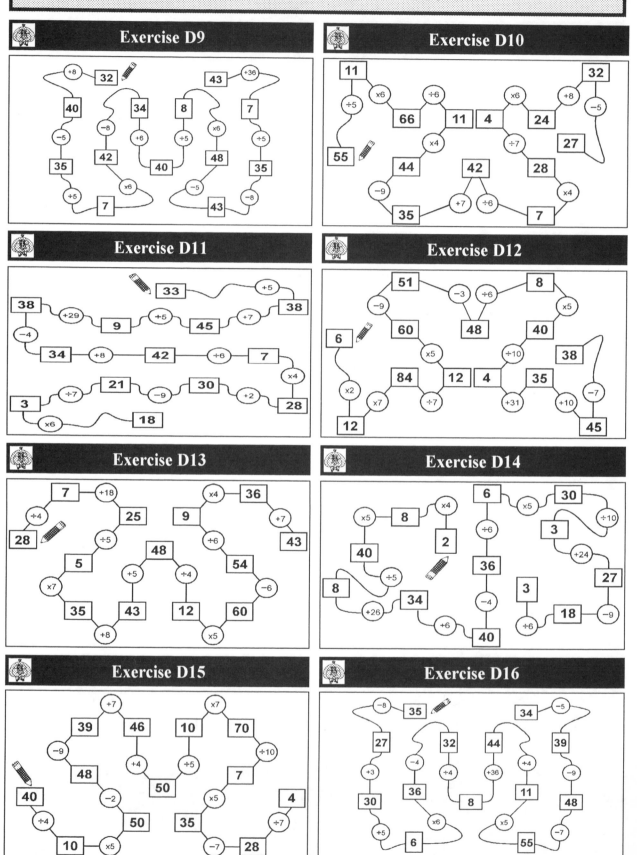

Answers to Section D

Children's Worksheets D17 - D24

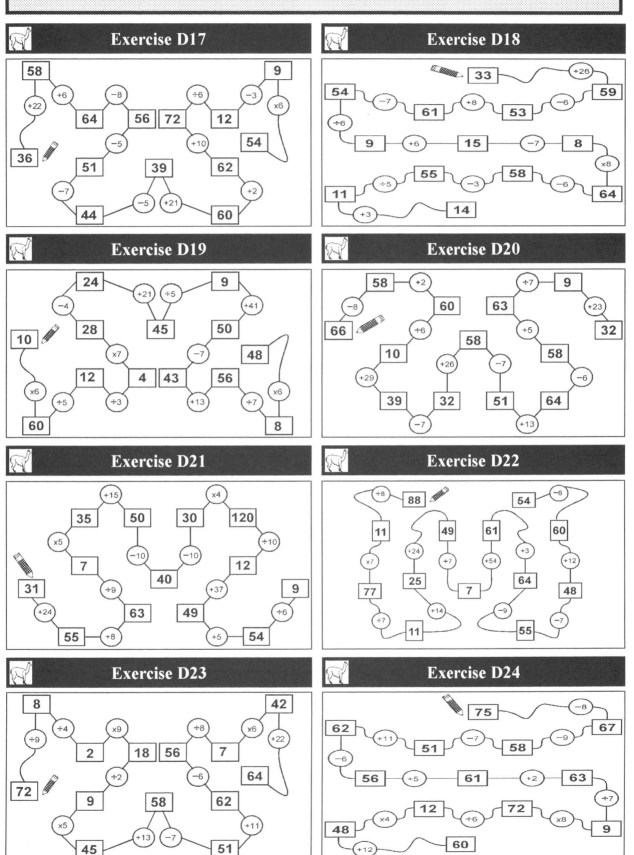

Answers to Section D

Children's Worksheets D25 - D32

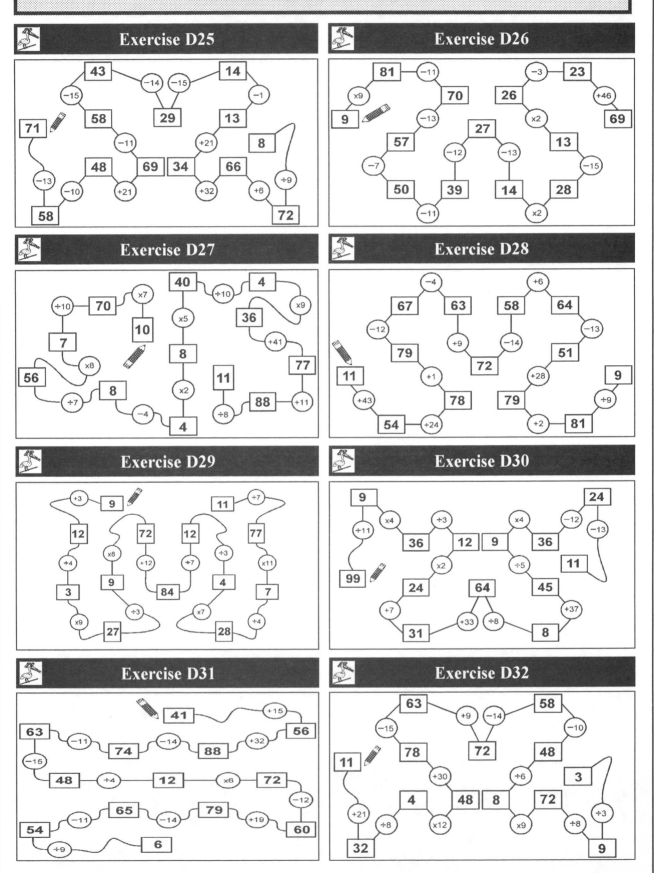

Answers to Section D

Children's Worksheets D33 - D40

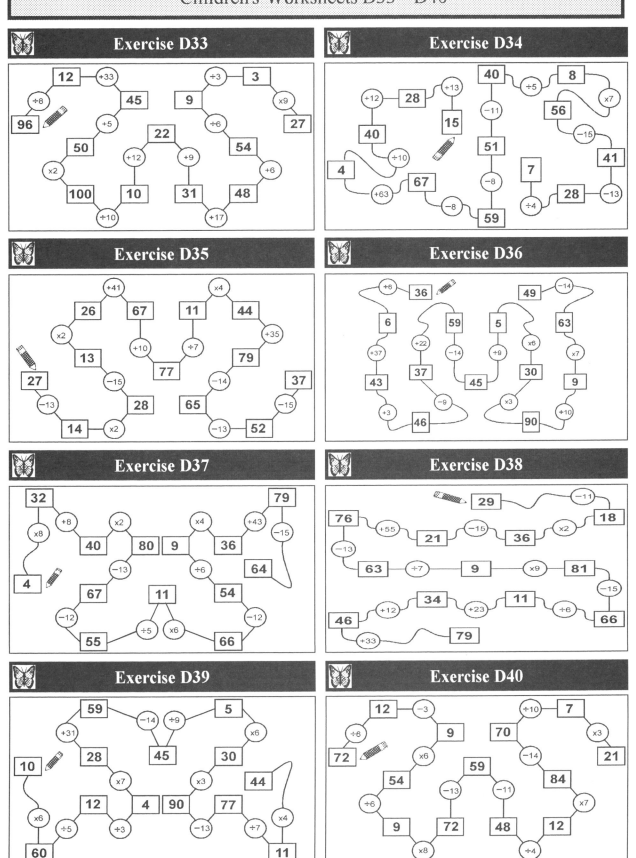

Answers to Section E

Children's Worksheets E1 - E8

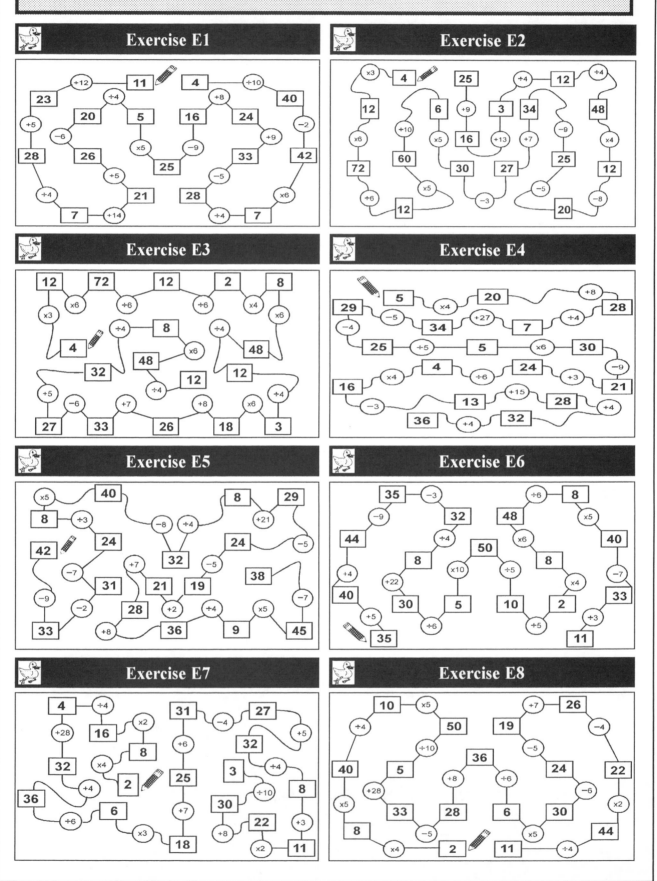

ONE-A-WEEK – *Mental Arithmetic Tests Book 3*

Answers to Section E

Children's Worksheets E9 - E16

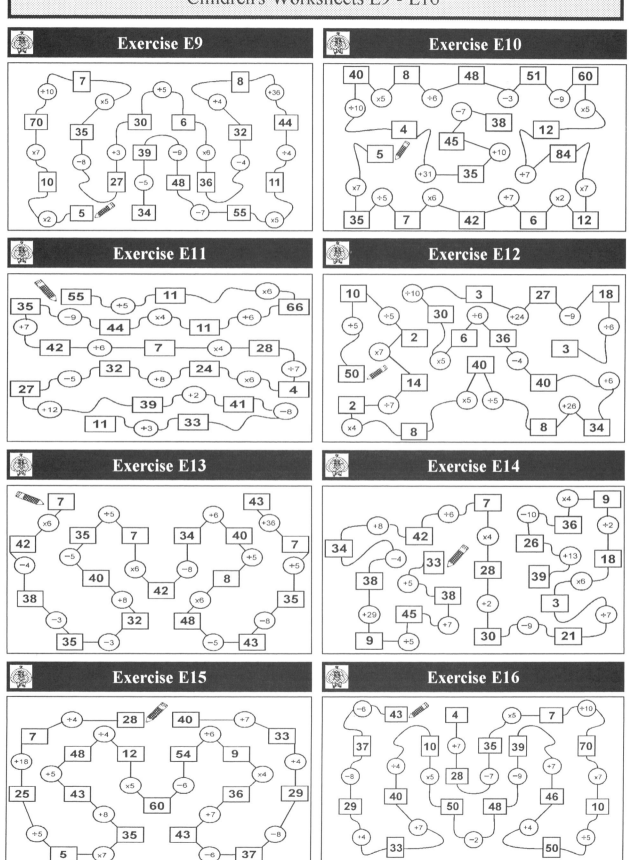

Answers to Section E

Children's Worksheets E17 - E24

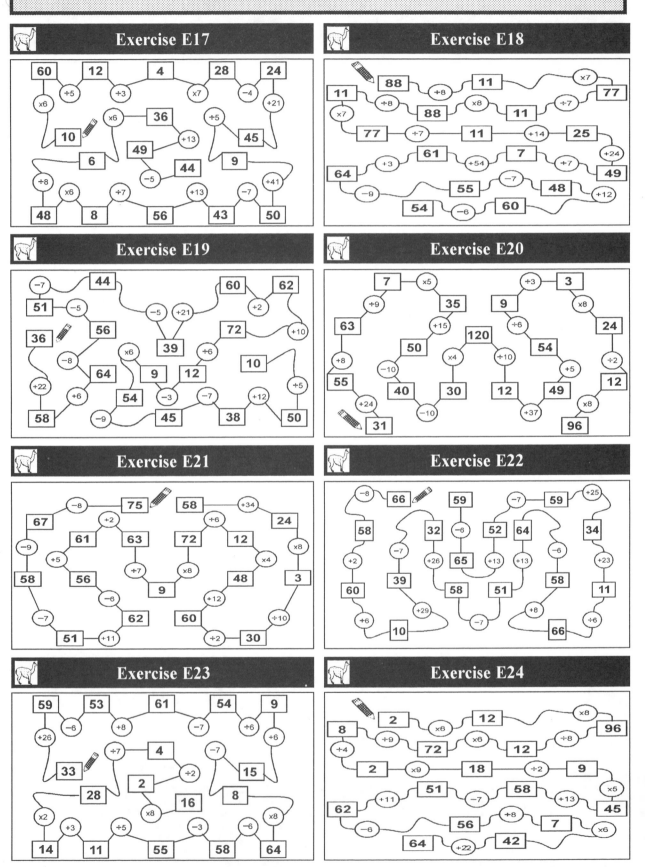

ONE-A-WEEK – *Mental Arithmetic Tests Book 3*

Answers to Section E

Children's Worksheets E25 - E32

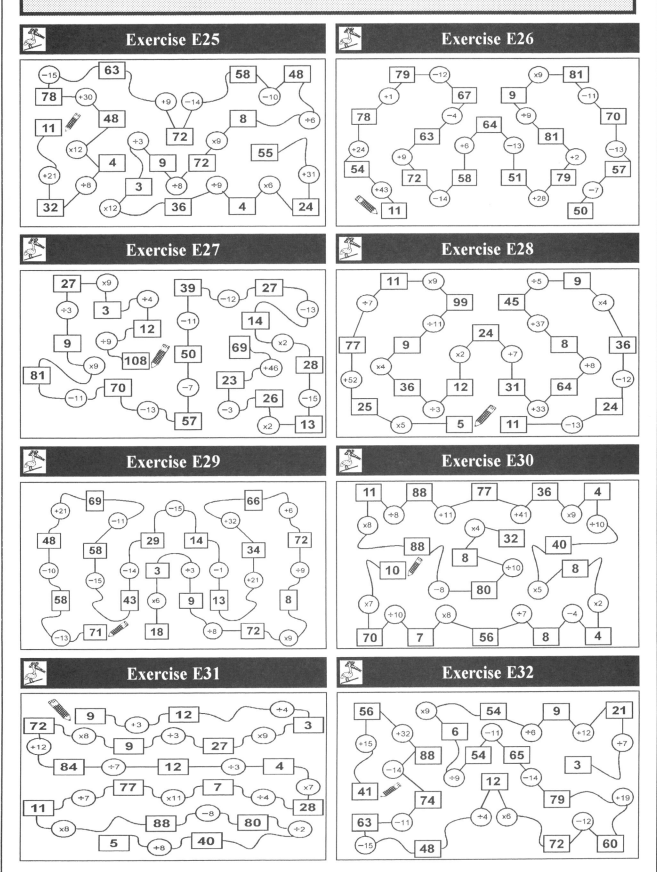

Answers to Section E

Children's Worksheets E33 - E40

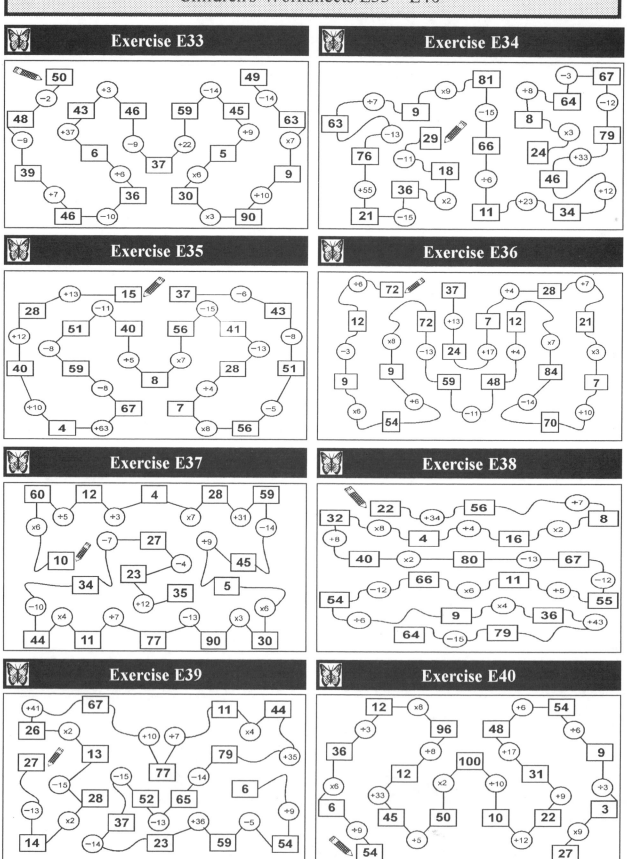